*Family Medical Costs and Voluntary
Health Insurance: A Nationwide Survey*

Family Medical Costs and Voluntary Health Insurance: A Nationwide Survey

ODIN W. ANDERSON, PH.D.

Health Information Foundation

with

JACOB J. FELDMAN

National Opinion Research Center

The Blakiston Division

McGraw-Hill Book Company, Inc.

New York   Toronto   London   1956

FAMILY MEDICAL COSTS AND VOLUNTARY HEALTH INSURANCE:
A NATIONWIDE SURVEY

FOREWORD

Few economic issues are of more interest to the American people today than the costs of medical care and how best to meet them. Indeed, in recent years, some of our most vigorous (and bitter) national debates have raged around these matters. To many it must seem strange that such concern should develop at a time when clearly more Americans are receiving better medical care and living longer and healthier lives than ever before. The situation, however, becomes much less paradoxical when the amazing strides taken by medical science in the past fifty years are viewed in the light of the social and economic conditions they create and in the total social context of our times. The short-term infectious disease has been conquered only to be replaced by the longer-term chronic disorder with greater total economic dislocation. The increasing pressures of the twentieth century have led to a rapidly mounting incidence of mental illness, often of indeterminate length and crushing expense. Maternal morbidity and mortality have been remarkably reduced, but only as the more expensive hospital delivery has been substituted for the less costly home delivery. The development of a concept of prevention of disease has meant greater utilization of health personnel and facilities and has required more frequent use of more complicated and costly equipment and procedures. The same pattern obtains in the treatment of large numbers of disorders once thought untreatable.

It must be remembered, however, that knowledge of the dramatic advances in medical science of the past fifty years has not been confined to the professionals in the field of health. Greater educational background and an active press have combined to make the present

v

generation of Americans better informed about matters of health than any in our national history. They know what has happened—what can be done—and they wish to share in the benefits to the fullest. In fact, they will not be denied. They seek expanded medical educational facilities to guarantee adequate numbers of trained personnel. They urge more medical research and support it generously with both tax and private dollars. They are midstride in building a hospital establishment second to none in the world. Indeed, the exciting tempo of medical progress has spread from the professionals in health to the consumer of medical care. He wants to join this chase of seemingly unlimited goals.

Withal, however, the American is practical, and it is therefore not surprising that he would not be so dazzled by the excitement of the chase as to forget fiscal realities. He properly insists on participating in the thinking in such affairs. He brings as his contribution the highly developed and much-cherished concept of insurance. After all, he says, if he can apply the principle of insurance to his home, his car, and his life, why not then to his health and that of his family? And why not indeed?

Unfortunately the matter has not been so simple. Serious actuarial problems have been raised by the shift in emphasis from infectious diseases to chronic disorders and mental illness. The role of government, which in recent years has been sharply expanded in other areas under a more liberal interpretation of the general-welfare clause of the Constitution, has caused bitter disagreement when evaluated in relationship to health services. "Adequate," when applied to medical service and insurance, has led to much confusion and difficulty. What is adequate medical care? What is an adequate surgical fee? Thus we can explain the current controversies in the field of medical economics.

Even if we cannot foretell the future, there are some predictions we can make with certainty. The American people will ultimately determine how their medical costs are to be handled. In a democracy this has always been true. The matter of financing medical care for our people is much too important to permit reckless political or selfish personal exploitation. And, finally, the wisest solution will come on the basis of objective, unemotional analysis of the facts.

This study by Anderson and Feldman represents a sound and useful effort to get the facts. It is the first such comprehensive study since the report of the Committee on the Costs of Medical Care in 1933, and it is particularly timely since it is really the first evaluation of medical costs in the light of the great development of voluntary health insurance. It is to be hoped that these unique data will be used constructively as an important contribution to a complex problem. The authors set out to prove only the power of fact, and this they have done in masterful fashion.

All who are interested in problems of health in our society must feel a debt to the Health Information Foundation and the American drug industry which supports it for underwriting this study. An important contribution to medical economics has been thereby made.

FRANKLIN D. MURPHY
Chancellor, University of Kansas

ACKNOWLEDGMENTS

During the time the Health Information Foundation was considering and later formulating the main outlines of a nationwide survey of family medical costs and voluntary health insurance, the Foundation had the good fortune of being able to consult with the following persons both individually and in committee meetings: L. E. Burney, M.D., Eli Ginzberg, Ph.D., Charles G. Hayden, M.D., Ira V. Hiscock, M.P.H., Sc.D., Ernest E. Irons, M.D., Solon T. Kimball, Ph.D., Franklin D. Murphy, M.D., Joseph G. Norby, J. Henry Smith, and E. A. Van Steenwyk.

I am also very grateful to the late Admiral W. H. P. Blandy (USN Ret.), president of Health Information Foundation until his death in 1954, and to Kenneth Williamson, former executive vice president of the Foundation, for the strong support given to the inauguration of this survey.

During the writing of the report and upon its completion, I had the privilege of discussing the content, the interpretations, and the generalizations with the following persons: George Bugbee, president, Health Information Foundation, C. Rufus Rorem, Ph.D., C.P.A., Franz Goldmann, M.D., and Louis I. Dublin, Ph.D.

In addition to Jacob J. Feldman, who was the staff member of the National Opinion Research Center, University of Chicago, most intimately concerned with the over-all technical aspects of the survey, other staff members of the Center who deserve mention are Sam Shapiro, William J. Cobb, Betty Roth Samuel, and Norma Watson.

ODIN W. ANDERSON

HIGHLIGHTS

The Survey

1. The survey was conducted in July, 1953, and is based on single interviews of 2,809 families in their homes.
2. The families comprise 8,846 individuals representing a national sample of the population of the United States, subdivided by age, sex, income, size of family, rural or urban residence, occupation, and region.
3. A sample of "area probability" type was used in this survey. It was drawn by the same methods as those used by the U.S. Bureau of the Census in the Current Population Survey. Estimates derived from it are, therefore, reliable within small margins.

Current Enrollment

1. Enrollment in all types of voluntary health insurance is over 100 million persons, or approximately 61 per cent of the population, and is increasing at a decreasing rate.
2. If coverage of 85 per cent of the population is assumed to be the goal, approximately 72 per cent of the potential has been covered by some type of health insurance.
3. Families with incomes over $5,000 are twice as likely to have some health insurance as families under $3,000, 80 per cent and 41 per cent respectively.
4. By industry there is a variation of 33 to 90 per cent with some type of health insurance.

5. In urban areas 70 per cent of the families are enrolled in some type of health insurance, and on farms, 45 per cent.

6. Seventy-seven per cent of the families with health insurance obtained it through their place of work or through another employed group.

7. Persons enrolled in groups tend to have higher incomes than persons enrolled as individuals.

8. Blue Cross subscribers tend to be more urban and have higher incomes than private-insurance subscribers.

9. There is a precipitous drop in enrollment after age 65.

Nationwide Charges for Personal Health Services

1. The total charges for all private personal health services were $10.2 billion, divided percentagewise as follows: physicians, 37 per cent; hospitals, 20 per cent; medicines, 15 per cent; other medical goods and services, 13 per cent; dentists, 16 per cent.

2. The percentages of charges covered by insurance were as follows: hospitals, 50 per cent; all physicians, 13 per cent; surgery, 38 per cent; obstetrics, 25 per cent. Other services were not listed because insurance coverage for them is negligible.

3. The mean gross charges per family for all personal health services were $207; for insured famiiles, $237; and for uninsured families, $154. The median charges in the same order were $110, $145, and $63. Families with incomes under $2,000 incurred mean charges of $130, and families with incomes over $7,500 incurred mean charges of $353.

4. The lower the family income, the greater was the percentage of income laid out for personal health services, ranging from a median of 6.1 per cent for incomes under $2,000 to one of 3.2 per cent for incomes over $7,500.

5. The mean charges per family by type of service were as follows: physicians, $78; hospitals, $41; medicines, $31; dentists, $33.

6. Families in large metropolitan areas incurred total charges for all personal health services of $237; families on farms, $178.

7. Among all families, 15 per cent were in debt to hospitals, physicians, dentists, and other providers of personal health services, and their average debt was $121, totaling $900 million.

8. The mean total charges for all personal health services for in-

dividuals were $65 and for each type of service were as follows: hospital, $13; physicians, $25; medicine, $10; dentists, $10.

9. Charges increased with age for all services except dentistry.

Distribution of Charges among Families and Individuals

1. Eight per cent of the families incurred no charges, and approximately 11 per cent of the families incurred charges exceeding $495, or 43 per cent of total charges for all families.

2. Fifty-three per cent of the families laid out less than 5 per cent of their incomes, and 2 per cent of the families incurred charges exceeding 50 per cent of their incomes.

3. Families incurred charges of over $195 by each type of service as follows: all services, 34 per cent of the families; all physicians' services, 11 per cent; surgery, 3 per cent; "other" physicians' services, 6 per cent; hospital, 6 per cent; medicines, 2 per cent; and dental, 4 per cent.

4. The higher the age, the greater the likelihood of relatively high charges, e.g., over $195.

5. The mean and median surgical charges per individual with charges were $101 and $69 respectively. Thirty-three per cent of the charges were less than $45, and 15 per cent were $195 and over.

6. Fifteen per cent of the families reported some medical indebtedness to providers of service, and 2 per cent reported indebtedness in excess of $195.

7. Families with insurance did not report less indebtedness than families without insurance.

Health Insurance and the Charges for Personal Health Services

1. Insured families received an average of $45 each in benefits from insurance, covering 19 per cent of charges for all personal health services. The lower the income among families with insurance, the higher was the proportion of charges paid by insurance: 26 per cent for incomes under $2,000, and 15 per cent for incomes over $7,500.

2. One half of the families incurring hospital charges and receiving insurance benefits had over 89 per cent of the hospital charges paid by insurance, and one half had less than 89 per cent paid by insurance.

3. Fifty-four per cent of the hospital admissions with hospital insurance and receiving benefits had over 90 per cent of their hospital charges covered.

4. One half of the families incurring charges for surgery and receiving insurance benefits had over 75 per cent of the charges paid by insurance, and one half had less than 75 per cent paid by insurance.

5. One half of the families incurring physicians' charges for obstetrics and receiving insurance benefits had over 60 per cent of the charges paid by insurance, and one half had less than 60 per cent paid by insurance.

Utilization of Hospital Care

1. The admission rate to hospitals for all persons was 12 per 100. For persons with insurance the rate was 14; for those without insurance, 9.

2. The male admission rate was 9 per 100; the female rate, 15.

3. Except for the age group from 18 to 34 (influenced by hospitalized maternity cases), the higher the age the greater was the hospital-admission rate. The age group under 5 had an admission rate of 8; the age group 65 and over, a rate of 13.

4. Approximately 18 per cent of all hospital admissions were for maternity care; among all females, 29 per cent of all admissions were for maternity; and among females in the age group from 18 to 34, 60 per cent of the admissions were for maternity.

5. Hospital-admission rates by income for all persons were virtually the same whether the incomes were high or low. Among the insured the admission rate among low-income persons was higher than for those in the upper-income groups: 21 for those under $2,000, and 12 for those over $7,500.

6. Among those insured in rural farm areas, the hospital-admission rate was 19 per 100, and among those insured in metropolitan areas the rate was 12.

7. The mean length of stay for all hospital admissions was 7.4 days. For those with insurance the length of stay was 7.0 days; for those without insurance, 8.3 days.

8. The older the person hospitalized, the longer was the mean length of stay: 5.3 days for the age group under 18, and 11.9 days for the age group over 55.

9. In 28 per cent of the hospital admissions, the patients stayed under 2 days; in 19 per cent, over 10 days; in 6 per cent, over 20 days.

10. There was a marked increase with increasing age in the percentage of admissions in which the patients stayed over 20 days; 3 per cent for those under 17 years of age, and 14 per cent for those over 55.

11. The number of hospital days per 100 persons for all persons per year was 90. For those with insurance there was 100 days per 100 persons, and for those without insurance, 70 days per 100 persons.

12. Persons over 55 made up 18 per cent of the population but utilized 30 per cent of the hospital days.

13. Thirty-two per cent of all hospital patients admitted occupied accommodations with room-and-board rates of $12 and over.

Utilization of Surgical and Other Services

1. For all persons there were 7 surgical procedures per 100 persons. For those with surgical insurance, the rate was 9; for those without insurance, 5.

2. By income groups there were only slight differences in surgery as income went up, but among all income groups with insurance, the group under $2,000 had a surgical rate of 15 and the group over $7,500 a rate of 8.

3. Persons with surgical insurance on farms had a surgical rate of 12 per 100, and persons with surgical insurance in metropolitan areas had a rate of 8.

4. The hospitalized tonsillectomy rate for insured persons under 17 years of age was 30 per 1,000; for those without insurance, 9.

5. The appendectomy rate for insured persons in the age group 6 to 54 was 11 per 1,000; for those without insurance, 5.

6. Thirty-four per cent of all persons consulted a dentist: 31 per cent of the males and 36 per cent of the females.

7. Seventeen per cent of the persons in families with incomes under $2,000 consulted a dentist, and 56 per cent of the persons with incomes over $7,500.

8. Insured persons in all income groups were more likely to consult a dentist than uninsured persons in corresponding income groups.

9. As estimated, 40 per cent of all persons did not consult a physician as out-of-hospital patients and 7 per cent of all persons consulted a physician 15 or more times.

Types of Insurers in Relation to Benefits and Utilization of Services

1. Both Blue Cross and private insurance paid approximately the same proportion of the hospital charges for their hospitalized subscribers covered under group insurance.
2. In individual hospital insurance Blue Cross covered a larger proportion of the hospital charges than private insurance.
3. In 43 per cent of the hospital admissions under Blue Cross the patient occupied hospital accommodations costing $12 a day or over; in 23 per cent of the admissions under private insurance the patient occupied such accommodations.
4. The average percentage of surgical charges covered by the various types of insurers were as follows: Blue Shield, 78 per cent; private group, 72 per cent; private nongroup, 66 per cent; independent, 94 per cent.

CONTENTS

CHAPTER *1*   *Introduction*

HISTORICAL BACKGROUND

In 1933 there was published the first nationwide survey of the distribution of the costs of medical care and morbidity among a representative sample of families in the United States.[1] In 1936 the U.S. Public Health Service published the results of a survey which was a study of morbidity of a large urban population sample. Costs of medical care were not part of the survey.[2]

These two studies, the first known as Report 26 of the Committee on the Costs of Medical Care, and the other as the National Health Survey, have provided the two chief sources of information on the costs of medical care and the extent of morbidity in the United States. A review of the data in speeches, papers, and reports of countless committees dealing with costs of medical care and extent of morbidity will reveal that invariably such data can be traced back to Report 26 of the Committee on the Costs of Medical Care and the National Health Survey of 1935–1936. Since these surveys there have been small-scale local studies of various kinds, but none on a national scale.[3]

[1] I. S. Falk, Margaret C. Klem, and Nathan Sinai, *The Incidence of Illness and the Receipt and Costs of Medical Care among Representative Families: Experiences in Twelve Consecutive Months during 1928–31*, Chicago, University of Chicago Press, 1933. (Publication of the Committee on the Costs of Medical Care, Report 26.)

[2] *The National Health Survey, 1935–1936: Significance, Scope and Method of a Nation-wide Family Canvass of Sickness in Relation to Its Social and Economic Setting*, U.S. Public Health Service, Division of Public Health Methods, 1938.

[3] Emily H. Huntington, *Cost of Medical Care: The Expenditures for Medical Care among 455 Families in the San Francisco Bay Area, 1947–1948*, Berkeley, Calif., University of California Press, 1951; I. S. Falk and Agnes W. Brewster, *Hospitalization and Insurance among Aged Persons: A Study Based on a Census*

It will be recalled that in 1932 voluntary health insurance as we know it today had hardly started. At that time even the principle of insurance or prepayment to spread the cost of a family's medical care had not yet been accepted and was a hotly debated issue.

One of the fundamental contributions of Report 26 of the Committee on the Costs of Medical Care was the finding that in a given year sickness was unpredictable for the individual family but relatively predictable for a group of families. Concurrently, since the costs of medical care were tied to sickness, it was shown that in a given year such costs were unpredictable for the individual family but relatively predictable for a group of families. For example, the average cost for all personal health services per family was $108 per year, but during the same year 10 per cent of the families incurred 41 per cent of all costs for personal health services in the United States. Some families incurred no costs, and others incurred costs of large amounts relative to their incomes.

During the thirties hospital prepayment plans sponsored by hospital

Survey in March, 1952, U.S. Social Security Administration, 1953 (Bureau Report 18); Dorothy McCamman and Agnes W. Brewster, "Voluntary Health Insurance Coverage of Aged Beneficiaries of Old-age and Survivors Insurance," *Social Security Bulletin*, **17**:3–11, August, 1954; Nathan Sinai and Dorothy E. Paton, *Hospitalization of the People of Two Counties: A Study of the Experience in Hillsdale and Branch Counties, Michigan, 1940–1945*, Ann Arbor, Mich., School of Public Health, University of Michigan, 1949 (Bureau of Public Health Economics, Research Series, no. 6); Arthur Weissman, "A Morbidity Study of the Permanente Health Plan Population: II. A Comparison of Utilization and Morbidity Data with Experience of Other Population Group," *Permanente Medical Bulletin*, **10**:17, August, 1952.

Many studies of rural counties have been done in New York State, Missouri, Michigan, Mississippi, and North Carolina. Selected ones are Donald G. Hay and Olaf F. Larson, *Use of Health Resources by Rural People in Two Western New York Counties, 1950*, Ithaca, N.Y., Cornell University, Department of Rural Sociology, U.S. Department of Agriculture cooperating, (Mimeograph Bulletin 31), June, 1952; Charles R. Hoffer, *Health and Health Services for Michigan Farm Families*, East Lansing, Mich., Michigan State College, Agricultural Experiment Station, September, 1948 (Special Bulletin 352); Marion T. Loftin and Robert E. Galloway, *The Use of Medical Services by Rural People in Four Mississippi Counties*, State College, Miss., Mississippi State College, Agricultural Experiment Station, March, 1954 (Sociology and Rural Life Series, no. 5); Harold F. Kaufman, *Use of Medical Services in Rural Missouri*, Columbia, Mo., University of Missouri, Agricultural Experiment Station, April, 1946 (Research Bulletin 400, Rural Health Series, no. 2); C. Horace Hamilton, *Rural Health and Medical Service in North Carolina: Papers and Preliminary Reports of Surveys, 1944–1949*, Raleigh, N.C., North Carolina State College, Agricultural Experiment Station, August, 1950 (Progress Report RS-9).

associations and medical prepayment plans sponsored by medical societies began to make headway. During the forties growth accelerated and private insurance also began to enter the field. Concurrently, the Congress, beginning in 1939, usually had national health-insurance bills for consideration.

This is not the place or the time to review the detailed development of the health-insurance movement, since there are other sources.[4] In any case, conservative estimates reveal that today (1955) around 100 million people in the United States are covered by some type of voluntary health insurance, whereas 15 years previously there had been only a handful.

PROBLEMS AND ISSUES TODAY

In all probability another nationwide survey would reveal, as did Report 26 of the Committee on the Costs of Medical Care, that in a year the costs of personal health services fall unevenly on a group of families, but a new element would be added—voluntary health insurance. So, in 1952 a second nationwide survey of families was formulated by the Health Information Foundation in collaboration with the National Opinion Research Center, University of Chicago, to reveal the distribution of the costs of personal health services among families, the extent of voluntary health insurance, and the impact of such insurance on costs.

[4] Joseph Hirsh, "The Compulsory Health Insurance Movement in the United States," *Social Forces*, **18**:102–114, October, 1939, and "Trends in the Development of Voluntary Health Insurance in the United States," *Southwestern Social Sciences Quarterly*, **21**:246–260, December, 1940; Helen H. Avnet, *Voluntary Medical Insurance in the United States: Major Trends and Current Problems*, New York, Medical Administration Service, 1943; C. Rufus Rorem, *Blue Cross Hospital Service Plans*, 2d ed., Chicago, American Hospital Association, 1944; J. T. Richardson and Stephen F. Austin, *The Origin and Development of Group Hospitalization in the United States, 1890–1940*, Columbia, Mo., University of Missouri, 1945 (University of Missouri Studies, vol. 20, no. 3); Nathan Sinai, Odin W. Anderson, and Melvin L. Dollar, *Health Insurance in the United States*, New York, The Commonwealth Fund, 1946; Louis S. Reed, *Blue Cross and Medical Service Plans*, U.S. Public Health Service, 1947; Franz Goldmann, *Voluntary Medical Care Insurance in the United States*, New York, Columbia University Press, 1948; Odin W. Anderson, "Compulsory Medical Care Insurance, 1910–1950," *Annals of the American Academy of Political and Social Science*, **273**:106–113, January, 1951; Maurice B. Hamovitch, "History of the Movement for Compulsory Health Insurance in the United States," *Social Service Review*, **27**:281–299, September, 1953.

There are many problems and issues today on which a nationwide survey of families would throw some light. The principle of insurance or prepayment for costs of personal health services is not an issue, but many issues arise in the application of the principle. Some are within the scope of this survey and others are not, but all are relevant and are related either to problems faced by families in meeting costs of medical care or to complex administrative problems faced by physicians, hospitals, and insurance agencies.

Two broad and profound problems will be facing voluntary health insurance for some time to come: one is expansion in terms of people covered, and the other is expansion in terms of benefits offered. Under the first problem, this survey will delineate "who has what" in terms of health insurance today. If near-universal coverage is the goal of voluntary health insurance, what is present-day coverage by age, sex, family income, residence, and other factors? Also, what type of health insurance prevails by type of service—hospital, surgery, and so on; by type of sponsorship—Blue Cross and Blue Shield, private insurance companies, and others?

Under the second problem—expansion in terms of benefits—it will be possible to reveal the economic impact of voluntary health insurance on our total costs for personal health services and on each category of service. This impact will be shown by insured and uninsured families, by age, sex, residence, and other factors. In addition to costs, there will be shown the influence insurance appears to have on utilization of services. Such information is obviously important, because there has been—and there still is today—a great deal of discussion as to what services and costs are "insurable" and "uninsurable" in the classical insurance sense. In any case it appears that services and costs regarded as "uninsurable" yesterday become "insurable" today, as cost and utilization data accumulate and as public pressure for broadening the scope of benefits continues.

Another debate which promises to continue for a long time, and which is an offshoot of the issue of limited benefits vs. so-called "comprehensive benefits," is the one of a financial concept of personal health services vs. what is known, for lack of a better term, as a health-service concept. The financial concept is presumed to be concerned primarily with the problem of paying for specified services which are unpredictable for a family and not with the provision of a complete health service embracing both curative and preventive services, such as physical examinations, as is supposed to be characteristic of the health-services concept.

This survey is limited to an analysis of the *financial* aspects of personal health services as reported by a representative sample of families throughout the nation. Sampling methods, size of sample, interview techniques, and schedule design are discussed in Appendix B. There is no attempt to determine the possible effect that present-day health insurance has exerted on the level of health of the families— an exceedingly difficult and complex task at best. Likewise, there is no attempt to enter into the administrative problems of present-day health insurance. Restated, the problem is: Given the present range of benefits offered by voluntary health insurance, what effects do such benefits have on spreading costs of personal health services and on the utilization of services?

CHAPTER 2   *Growth of Voluntary Health Insurance*

No attempt will be made in this book to document the details of the growth of voluntary health insurance.[1] Another source is available for this purpose.[2] It is in order, however, to present some of the highlights of the growth in terms of people covered and in terms of range of benefits offered leading up to the current picture. Thus our current coverage and benefits offered will be seen in a better perspective.

DEVELOPMENT BY TYPE OF SERVICE

Present-day voluntary health insurance had its primary origin in hospital care. The Blue Cross idea originated in the early thirties in Texas and was taken up in Minnesota and New Jersey, followed by Ohio, Pennsylvania, and New York.

Also, during the same time there were the beginnings of the cooperative health-service plans such as the one in Elk City, Oklahoma. In the latter thirties the Blue Shield medical-care plans were organized in Michigan and California at the same time that the Blue Cross plans sponsored by the hospitals began to gather momentum in their number and growth.

By 1940 several types of health insurance, in terms of range of benefits offered and manner of organization of service, had emerged, which form the bases for the problems and issues today. There were,

[1] In this report "health insurance" denotes insurance against costs of personal health services only and excludes insurance against loss of income because of disability.

[2] Oscar N. Serbein, Jr., *Paying for Medical Care in the United States*, New York, Columbia University Press, 1953, chap. XXXIV, pp. 376–392.

and are, the Blue Cross hospital plans grafted on, so to speak, to the existing structure of hospital service. There were the Blue Shield plans which were, and are, grafted on the present practice of medicine, particularly in-hospital physicians' services. Private insurance companies were beginning to enter the picture and were differing primarily from the two foregoing in that they had no contractual relationships with the providers of service, i.e., the hospitals and physicians, as did the Blue Cross and Blue Shield plans, respectively. There are other differences which need not be gone into here.[3]

There are interesting and noteworthy exceptions to the usual Blue Shield pattern on the part of medical-society-sponsored medical prepayment plans. Canadian plans such as Windsor Medical Services in Windsor, Ontario, and the Medical Bureaus of the states of Washington and Oregon offer a wide range of physicians' services on a prepaid basis with no apparent basic change in the present structure of medical practice.

A type of plan which differs completely from the foregoing health-insurance arrangements is found in the group health plans which are group-practice units tied to prepayment. The physicians are on salaries with offices in the group-practice units. They represent a rearrangement of the structure of medical practice from so-called "solo practice" on a fee-for-service basis to group practice on a salary basis. The group-practice plans provide a wider range of physicians' services on a prepaid basis than do the Blue Shield plans generally. Well-known examples are the Health Insurance Plan of Greater New York (HIP), the Group Health Association in Washington, D.C., the Kaiser Permanente Foundation in California, and the Ross-Loos Clinic in California.

The sequence of stages by type of service in which health insurance evolved can be traced roughly, but the outlines are still clear. The stages reflect the changes in thinking as to the feasibility of insuring or prepaying certain personal health services. Before tracing these stages, however, it may be well to outline the components of what is nebulously known as "comprehensive" medical care.

[3] See, for example, William S. McNary, "An Evaluation of Blue Cross Plans," Charles G. Hayden, "An Evaluation of Blue Shield Plans," and John H. Miller, "An Evaluation of Medical Care Plans Underwritten by Insurance Companies," in *Building America's Health: Financing a Health Program for America*, The President's Commission on the Health Needs of the Nation, A Report to the President, vol. 4, pp. 42–65.

OUTLINE OF THE COMPONENTS OF PERSONAL HEALTH SERVICES

A. Hospital care
    1. Room, board, and general nursing service
    2. Type of accommodation
        a. Private
        b. Semiprivate
        c. Ward
    3. Operating room
    4. Delivery room
    5. Routine medications, dressings, etc.
    6. Radiological services
    7. Anesthetist (if on the hospital staff)
    8. Pathologist (if on the hospital staff)
    9. Laboratory services

B. Physicians' services
    1. Home, office, and hospital calls
    2. Surgery
    3. Obstetrical
    4. Diagnostic and therapeutic services using special equipment such as X-ray

C. Private-duty nursing services

D. Dentists' services (classified by dentures, fillings, extractions, etc.)

E. Drugs and medications

F. Nursing and convalescent homes

G. Appliances

This outline can very likely be expanded, but it probably contains the core of what are regarded as personal health services today as differentiated from the usual public health services, but not too clearly defined. It should be noted that services of housekeepers in case of a disabled housewife, special diets and vitamins, and similar services and goods are excluded. The survey deals with the items in the outline only, with the exception of nursing and convalescent homes.

The sequence of stages by type of service is as follows: (1) the first stage was the full range of services regarded as hospital services, disregarding limitations as to number of days, use of auxiliary services, and others; (2) the next service to enter into prepayment was in-hospital surgery. These two services were, and still are, regarded as the chief justification for health insurance, since they are recognized as being unpredictable and high-cost services for which a family could not budget easily, the so-called "insurable" services. A later expansion of surgical services was the inclusion of surgery in physicians' offices, classified as minor surgery even though it was not relatively expensive; and emergency care, wherever treatment took place, was included.

At the same time that hospital and surgical services were introduced, in-hospital obstetrical services were included. There were many debates among insurance circles as to the advisability of insuring obstetrical care, an allegedly predictable service for the individual family, but subscriber demand apparently dictated its inclusion. So, already the classical concepts of "insurability" were being changed, but it should be added that early Blue Cross leaders never pretended that hospital care was "insurable" in the classical insurance sense. They were thinking of a relatively painless method of paying hospital bills on the part of the patients as well as a stable financial base for hospital care.

It is a simple matter to outline the components of personal health services on paper, but it is difficult to keep them separate in a prepayment or insurance plan, some services prepaid and others not. The tendency has been to broaden the range of benefits for several reasons. Thus, in-hospital physicians' services in addition to surgery now constitute a standard pattern in Blue Shield plans and private insurance-company contracts throughout the country. In the late thirties, physician-sponsored medical plans in Michigan and California experimented with home and office calls; the financial results were reportedly disastrous, inhibiting further experimentation for a number of years until recently. In the meantime, however, as stated earlier, Windsor, Washington, and Oregon have been operating physician-sponsored medical plans covering home and office care for 20 to 25 years and—as measured by solvency, at least—have been successful.

Now there is a great deal of pressure for expansion of the range of benefits offered in physicians' services. The "major-medical" type of contract offered by private insurance companies and also by Blue Cross and Blue Shield is symptomatic of this pressure. It is feared by organized medicine and the Blue Shield plans that expansion of physicians' services to include home and office calls and outpatient diagnostic services will entail a reorganization of medical practice along the lines of group practice tied to prepayment and a salaried medical staff. This is a very real fear because of the apparent difficulties of controlling costs and volume of services in a fee-for-service type of arrangement, since the salary method of payment is rejected by the overwhelming majority of practicing physicians.

There are many other smaller issues that have emerged in this period of expansion of benefits offered in a prepayment or insurance plan, but the two chief and related ones are (1) "comprehensive" benefits vs. limited benefits; and (2) capitation or salary vs. fee-for-service, and group practice vs. solo practice.

SEQUENCE OF STAGES BY RESIDENCE AND OCCUPATION OF SUBSCRIBERS AND DEPENDENTS

The voluntary-health-insurance system as we know it today can be said to have started with the "white-collar" segment of the population employed as a group. It was a group that had a stable income and employment, coupled with characteristics of thrift, foresight, and a high level of health consciousness. Very shortly, however, the population backbone of the voluntary-health-insurance movement became the people in industry with a common employer in groups above a certain size. This was necessary in order to prevent self-selection of health risks and to facilitate easy premium collection such as automatic payroll deduction. Also, there was an early tendency to enroll the employee only and not his dependents, since dependents utilize more services than the employee himself. Again, very shortly, inclusion of dependents became a common practice and is now quite standard.

Consequently, voluntary health insurance, with few exceptions, became an urban phenomenon, and more specifically one of employed groups in urban areas. Later more attention was paid to so-called "individual enrollment" of farm groups and of the self-employed in urban areas.

GROWTH TRENDS BY TYPE OF SERVICE AND INSURER

In measuring the growth of voluntary health insurance 1940 may be used as a base year, because by that time voluntary-health-insurance enrollment was beginning to be a felt factor in the financing of personal health services. At that time, over 9 per cent of the population was carrying some type of hospital insurance, 4 per cent of the population had some type of surgical insurance, and slightly over 2 per cent had some type of medical insurance, such as in-hospital physicians' services, at least. By the end of 1954 the percentages were roughly over 60 per cent, 50 per cent, and 25 per cent respectively.

It will be noted that surgical-insurance coverage is beginning to approach hospital-insurance coverage, and some type of other physicians' service is also increasing rapidly. At the present time so-called "comprehensive physicians' services" plans are carried by approximately 3 to 4 per cent of the population.

In the growth of enrollment by type of insurer—private insurance companies, and Blue Cross and Blue Shield—it will be noted that Blue Cross hospital-plan enrollment exceeded that of private insurance companies until around 1950. At that time, private insurance became equal to Blue Cross, and since then it has been steadily gaining. In surgical and other insurance covering physicians' services, private insurance companies have always been ahead of Blue Shield, at least since 1939.

CHAPTER *3*　　*Current Enrollment*

Since this survey was carried out in July, 1953, its figures for enroll-ment in voluntary health insurance are already out of date to a de-gree. In that month, an estimated 57 per cent of the population, or 88 million people, had some type of hospital insurance. The Health In-surance Council,[1] at the end of 1952, estimated an enrollment of approximately 92 million under hospital insurance according to in-surance-company records. The difference in the estimates is discussed in Appendix B and so need not concern us here. In any case, in a population of 155 million outside institutions in the United States, a difference of this size is not a serious matter in the over-all picture. The Health Insurance Council's most recent estimate places the hos-pital-insurance total at almost 102 million.[2] This underscores the fact that voluntary-health-insurance enrollment is still growing.

In a report of this nature no particular stress will be placed on last-minute information, as it were, because of the constantly changing voluntary-health-insurance scene. What would seem to be more im-portant is to attempt to show the relative proportions of health insur-ance by type of service and type of insurer, and the distribution of insurance by region, residence, age, sex, and related factors. It would seem to be a reasonable assumption that these relative proportions will remain somewhat the same for some time to come, even though the absolute number of insured people will rise during the next few years.

Thus it is important to know the relative strengths, as measured by

[1] *Accident and Health Coverage in the United States as of December 31, 1952,* New York, Health Insurance Council, September, 1953.

[2] *The Extent of Voluntary Health Insurance Coverage in the United States as of December 31, 1954,* Preliminary Report on Annual Survey, Health Insurance Council, New York, 1955.

12

number of subscribers, of the various types of insurers in order to note the direction that voluntary health insurance is taking as to sponsorship, range of benefits, and segments of the population covered. Also, in what regions and occupations are the various types of insurers most active, and in what income groups? Facts on these matters form the basis for discussion of many of the problems and issues in the health-insurance field today.

NATIONAL AND REGIONAL ENROLLMENT

Private insurance companies are exceeding Blue Cross hospital enrollment and appear to be increasing at a faster rate as well. In surgical and limited medical insurance, private insurance companies are well ahead of Blue Cross and Blue Shield. Around 3 per cent of the population is covered by substantially complete physicians' services. Insurance for costs incurred because of so-called "dread-disease" and "major-medical" expense continues to grow, making the figures of 4 per cent and about 3 per cent, respectively, of the population covered by such insurance very unstable (see Table A-1).

The enrollment by regions in the United States shows some variation. A higher percentage of the population is enrolled in both hospital and surgical insurance in the Northeast and North Central regions than in the South and West (see Table A-2).

The distribution of health insurance by type of enrollment—group or individual—is of significance because of the greater ease in selling through groups and the generally greater range of benefits offered. Individual or so-called "nongroup" type of enrollment accounts for well over one-third of the voluntary-health-insurance enrollment today. Also, private insurance companies underwrite twice as many people on an individual basis as do Blue Cross and Blue Shield in hospital and surgical insurance (see Table A-3).

ENROLLMENT BY SOCIAL AND ECONOMIC CHARACTERISTICS

Family Income

One hears a great deal about protection against costs of personal health services for the "middle" income group, since it is often said that the poor and the well to do receive good medical care without insurance, but the family in the middle needs some method of pooling costs. Also, one hears that voluntary health insurance is designed for "low" income as well as for "middle" income.

For the purpose of meeting costs of personal health services, it is difficult to determine "low," "middle," and "high" income because they must be related to ability to pay for an accepted standard of living as well as for unpredictable costs of personal health services. Thus no definitions are proposed here, but the percentage of enrollment in some type of insurance by family income will be presented.

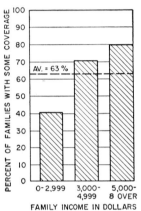

Fig. 1. Percentage of families with voluntary health insurance, by income groups (see Table A-4).

Among families earning under $3,000 a year, 41 per cent have some type of health insurance; between incomes of $3,000 and $5,000, the proportion increases to 71 per cent; $5,000 and over, 80 per cent. Approximately a third of the families are in each of these three income groups. It is apparent that there is quite a break between the family income under and over $3,000. The group under $3,000 contains more old and single people and farmers than the income groups over $3,000.

The median income in families with some insurance is approximately $4,500, which means that half these families earn more than $4,500 and half earn less. The median income for families without some protection is $2,700. Approximately 16 per cent of the individuals in the sample were in families which had incomes of less than $2,000. Since 5 to 6 million people at any one time receive public assistance, they are part of the 24 million individuals in families with under $2,000 a year income, or between 20 and 25 per cent of this income group. Those receiving public assistance are not in the health-insurance market. It is of significance to note, however, that 31 per cent of the families under $2,000 have at least one member with some type of health insurance, although by any standard such an income group must be living close to subsistence.

The distribution of hospital insurance by income and by group enrollment or individual enrollment shows clearly that the lower-income families tend to carry individual insurance if they have any insurance at all.

In the income group under $2,000, it should be noted that 62 per cent of those with insurance are enrolled as individuals, and the proportion drops precipitously at $2,000 and over. Likewise, it is of significance that hospital-insurance enrollment among incomes under $3,500 is predominantly underwritten by private insurance, and above $3,500 Blue Cross tends to be more common. Paralleling the above, Blue Cross and private hospital insurance are quite similar in the in-

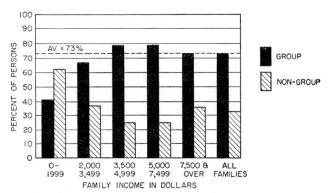

Fig. 2. Percentage distribution of persons covered by hospital insurance, by income and type of enrollment (see Table A-5).

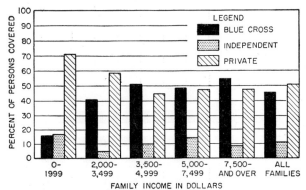

Fig. 3. Percentage distribution of persons covered by hospital insurance, by type of insurer and income (see Table A-6).

come composition of their group enrollment, but in individual or non-group enrollment private insurance coverage is more common among lower-income groups than is Blue Cross.

Residence

It will be recalled that 57 per cent of the population was enrolled in some type of hospital insurance. By residence the enrollment is as follows:

Urban................ 64%
Rural nonfarm.......... 52
Rural farm............. 38

The percentage of families with any type of insurance is 63 per cent for the country and by residence is as follows:

Urban................ 70%
Rural nonfarm.......... 57
Rural farm............. 45

When hospital-insurance enrollment is classified by both residence and type of insurer, Blue Cross enrollment is more characteristic of metropolitan areas than private insurance, and the reverse is true as residence becomes increasingly rural.

Industry

The main earners in the families who are employed either by private employers or by government, and therefore belong to em-

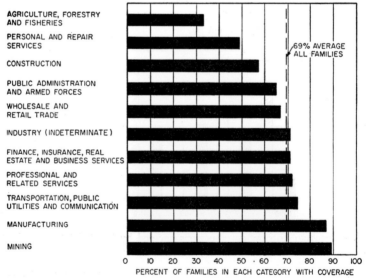

Fig. 4. Percentage of families with voluntary health insurance, by industry of main earner (see Table A-9).

ployed groups, have generally a larger percentage of people enrolled than do the self-employed. On an average, 78 per cent of families whose main earner works for private employers have some type of health insurance, 71 per cent of those in government service, and 46 per cent of those self-employed. When enrollment is broken down by industry, there is a range of 33 to 90 per cent of families with a main earner in specified industries enrolled in some type of insurance. The self-employed and people employed in very small groups are a particular problem facing voluntary health insurance today and very likely for some time to come. The relatively low enrollment of people in this segment of the population is not necessarily a measure of the unavailability of health insurance to them, but it certainly indicates that they are not availing themselves of insurance for one reason or another. The unavoidably high cost of acquisition, the waiting periods, and the limitations on benefits to prevent self-selection are common problems to be faced in the enrollment of the self-employed groups, in contrast to enrollment of employed groups.

Education

When the extent of enrollment in some type of voluntary health insurance is broken down by the level of education of the main earner, it is found that the higher the educational attainment, the greater the likelihood of health-insurance coverage. Educational attainment is, of course, associated with income, level of living, residence, and other factors (see Table A-10).

Approximately 18 per cent of the main wage earners have 6 years of schooling or less. The majority, 64 per cent, have from 7 to 12 years of schooling. Families with main earners reporting no schooling are covered in 35 per cent of the instances; families reporting 4 years of college or more had insurance in 76 per cent of the instances.

Age and Sex

Families with female heads are less likely to have any health insurance than those with male heads. This is undoubtedly a reflection of lower income of female heads and the unlikelihood of their being employed in groups with health insurance such as mining and manufacturing. Sixty-six per cent of the families with male heads and 48 per cent of the families with female heads have at least one member with some type of health insurance.

When coverage is broken down by persons instead of families, it will be noted that 57 per cent of both males and females carry some type of insurance. Among persons of both sexes there is decreasing coverage with increasing age.

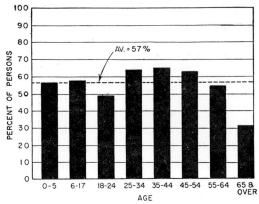

Fig. 5. Percentage of persons with hospital insurance, by age (see Table A-11).

OTHER ENROLLMENT MATTERS

Multiple Enrollment

When a large proportion of the population is enrolled in hospital and surgical insurance, and when a great many health-insurance agencies are active, some degree of duplication of coverage can be expected. In some instances a person enrolled in a group might also have bought some insurance on an individual basis. In other instances, an individual may have purchased more than one hospital or surgical contract on an individual basis in order to be sure that insurance would pay most or all of the charges.

In insurance circles, duplication of coverage is regarded as a problem if such duplication leads to overinsurance, i.e., insurance in excess of the cost of the services insured. On a national basis, 10 per cent of the individuals enrolled in hospital insurance had more than one hospital policy. Approximately 11 per cent of the individuals with surgical insurance have more than one policy.

Place of Enrollment

Table 1 shows how the subscriber first happened to acquire a health-insurance policy. Approximately 77 per cent of those families which currently have some insurance originally obtained one of their present policies through a group. This figure is obtained by adding the first, second, and fifth items and correcting for duplication. It will be noted that 14 per cent of the families with some coverage obtained one of their present policies by being directly approached by an insurance agent, and only 5 per cent by response to direct-mail, newspaper, or radio advertising.

Table 1. How Subscriber First Happened to Get the Plans or Policies

How policy was secured	Per cent of families* in which at least one policy was secured as below

(All families with insurance = 100%)

Through place of work or union	68
Through other group	5
Approached by insurance agent	14
A relative or friend took it out for the covered family member	3
Transferred from group to individual after leaving place of work or other group	8
Subscriber's "initiative" in response to direct-mail, newspaper, or radio advertising	5
Subscriber's "initiative" in response to advice or suggestions of friends, relatives, etc	5
Subscriber's "initiative" after heavy medical expense in family	1
Subscriber's "initiative" after "scare" outside family	1

* Each of the 1,780 families with some type of health insurance was asked this question about each of the family's insurance policies; therefore the percentages add up to more than 100%.

How Policies Were Held

In the foregoing it was indicated that about 77 per cent of the families obtained one of their present health-insurance policies through a group of some kind. Table 2 shows the ways in which health-insurance policies were held at the time of the survey.

Table 2. Ways in Which Policies Are Currently Held

How policy is held	Per cent of families* in which at least one plan or policy is held in this way

(All families with insurance = 100%)

Through group at place of work	68
Through a Farm Bureau or other farmer's group	2
Through other group—grocers' association, plumbers' union, ministers' association, social or fraternal group	4
Currently retired—covered by "same plan" as when was working	1
Originally got the plan or policy through place of work or through other group but now holds it individually	8
Individually	32

* These percentages add to more than 100% because some of the 1,780 families with insurance have more than one kind of policy.

Approximately 32 per cent of the families with insurance carried at least one nonconverted individual policy, while 8 per cent carried a converted policy. There was some attrition from the 77 per cent because of the 8 per cent (the fifth item) who had changed from a group policy to an individual policy, so-called "conversions."

Employer Contributions

In order to determine employer contributions to the cost of health-insurance premiums, only families who had health-insurance policies through a group at place of work were included, because it was assumed that those who had individual policies paid the whole premium themselves.

The extent of employer contribution could be determined only to the extent of dividing the families into three groups: (1) some employer contribution; (2) no employer contribution; and (3) total employer contribution. Among the families with at least one health-insurance policy held through a work group it was found that:

1. 49 per cent received some contribution from an employer but also paid some health-insurance premiums themselves.
2. 10 per cent had their total health-insurance premiums paid by employers.
3. 41 per cent received no contribution from employers.

It was further found that 44 per cent of the families whose only hospital insurance was a Blue Cross group hospital plan had part or the entire premium paid by the employer, and 72 per cent of the families whose only hospital insurance was group private hospital insurance had an employer contribution.

CHAPTER 4 *Nationwide Charges for Personal Health Services*

This chapter will present the charges for personal health services on a nationwide basis with no attempt to show the range of such charges, from nothing to large amounts, among families and individuals. When costs of personal health services are viewed primarily in terms of the national economy and family income, how do such costs stand out? Later chapters will present the impact of costs of personal health services on families and individuals.

NATIONWIDE TOTALS BY TYPES OF SERVICE

It can be estimated on the basis of the reports from a representative sample of American people that during the 12 months preceding July, 1953, incurred charges for all personal health services were in the neighborhood of $10.2 billion. This is exclusive of the $2 billion or so paid out by all levels of government for direct services. The $10.2 billion thus represents the charges for private personal health services paid out of pocket by the American public directly and by voluntary health insurance on their behalf.

In an absolute sense $10.2 billion is a great deal of money under any circumstances, even in as productive an economy as that of the United States. It is clear that the provision of health services is one of the "big businesses" in the United States, involving about 5,000 general hospitals, 180,000 practicing physicians, 78,000 dentists, 335,000 graduate nurses, and pharmacists, dietitians, physical therapists, laboratory technicians, and others and their training and research facilities. Behind these providers of service stand 80 medical schools, 42 dental schools, and almost 1,200 schools of nursing with their research and teaching facilities, the pharmaceutical, chemical, and drug industries, the hospital equipment and supply manufacturers, the appliance manufacturers, and others.

As was stated previously, $10.2 billion is a great deal of money. But what does it mean in terms of the national income and personal income, and how is it divided among the various types of services that make up our personal health services? In national terms, $10.2 billion is only 4 to 5 per cent of the total national income. This percentage has remained remarkably stable during the last 25 years. Although

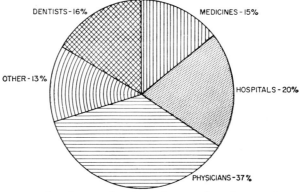

Fig. 6. Percentage distribution of estimated national total gross charges incurred by families for personal health services and goods (see Table A-13).

the costs and volume of services have risen during this period, other sectors of the American standard of living have also risen, so that the costs of personal health services have remained in a constant relationship proportionately. From 1929 to 1951 expenditures for personal health services from private sources were consistently about 4 per cent of all consumer expenditures. In fact, the percentages varied only between 4.1 and 4.4 per cent.[1]

The $10.2 billion are distributed among the various types of services as in Fig. 6. The proportion of the medical dollar going for physicians' services is almost twice as great as the proportion for hospital services. Over the past 25 years there has been a clear tendency for the proportions shared by these two services to converge,

[1] Oscar N. Serbein, Jr., *Paying for Medical Care in the United States,* New York, Columbia University Press, 1953, p. 49.

indicating that hospital care is taking a larger share of the medical dollar and physicians' services a smaller share.[2]

It will be noted that physicians' and hospital charges account for 57 per cent of all charges for personal health services. It is these services which are regarded today as so-called "insurable" services, with some debate as to the feasibility and wisdom of insuring home and office calls and outpatient diagnostic services. In any case, there is general agreement as to covering surgical and obstetrical services, and if all physicians' services other than surgery and obstetrics are added to hospital care, these services account for 31 per cent of all charges for personal health services.

Within physicians' services only, the costs of services on a national basis appear as in Table 3. In terms of costs, surgery and obstetrics

Table 3. Estimated Nationwide Total Gross Charges Incurred by Families for Physicians' Services
July, 1952, through June, 1953

Type of physicians' service*	Amount, billions	Per cent
All physicians................	$3.8	100
Surgery.....................	0.8	21
Obstetrics...................	0.4	11
Other physicians.............	2.6	68

* Definition of physicians' services in Table A-13.

account for 32 per cent of all physicians' services, indicating that other such services make up two-thirds of all physicians' costs. Surgery and obstetrics are virtually in-hospital physician costs, but it is not possible

[2] The definitions of the services and the methods by which costs were allocated in the present study are discussed in the footnotes to Table A-13. Variations from the estimates of the U.S. Department of Commerce are also explained. In 1930, for example, physicians' costs accounted for 32 per cent of the medical dollar, and hospital costs 14 per cent. Recently from the same basic source, i.e., U.S. Department of Commerce, physicians' costs accounted for 29 per cent of the medical dollar and hospital costs also 29 per cent. Sources: Frank G. Dickinson, *Medical Care Expenditures, Prices and Quantity, 1930–1950*, Chicago, American Medical Association, 1951 (Bureau of Medical Economic Research, Bulletin 87); "Voluntary Insurance against Sickness: 1948–53 Estimates," *Social Security Bulletin,* 17:3–9, December, 1954, Table 4. Presumably, if similar methods of determining costs had been applied at intervals over the past 25 years as were applied in the present study, physicians' and hospital costs would show a convergence, although not resulting in equal percentages. It is, of course, possible that this trend will continue.

in the present survey to separate "other" physicians' services in terms of in-hospital and out-of-hospital proportions. Such a separation would be useful because current health-insurance contracts are concerned largely with illnesses treated in hospitals.

NATIONWIDE TOTAL CHARGES AND HEALTH INSURANCE

It was stated that the private personal health services charges today total $10.2 billion. According to estimates made in the report of the President's Commission on the Health Needs of the Nation,[3] it would appear that the various levels of government account for approximately $2 billion for direct services. Since it was found that insurance contributes $1.5 billion, this sum plus $2 billion by government indicate that approximately 29 per cent of the charges for all personal health services in this country do not come from the patients directly. Also, this percentage does not include the undetermined "free care" contributed by physicians, hospitals, and others.

This report, however, is concerned primarily with the total charges for personal health services rendered to private patients and with the contribution of voluntary health insurance to those charges. On a national basis, voluntary health insurance accounts for $1.5 billion of the $10.2 billion mentioned previously, or 15 per cent of all charges for private personal health services. As present trends continue, this percentage can be expected to increase as evident in a recent estimate for the calendar year 1953 by the Social Security Administration. It is estimated that approximately 20 per cent of the costs of private personal health services is covered by insurance.[4] If this figure implies that 80 or 85 per cent of the charges, as the case may be, are still left to be covered by voluntary health insurance, it should be borne in mind that dental services, medicines, appliances, and other services not usually covered by insurance are included in our concept of personal health services. It is unlikely that the most comprehensive prepayment plans in existence cover more than 50 per cent of the costs of the whole range of personal health services sought by families and individuals, except a few that have added dental benefits.

[3] *Building America's Health: Financing a Health Program for America,* A Report to the President, vol. 4, Table 2.1, p. 153.
[4] *Social Security Bulletin,* 17:3–9, December, 1954, Table 7. For 1948 the Social Security Administration estimated slightly over 8 per cent, indicating a gain of 150 per cent in 5 years.

It is, therefore, more meaningful to break down the totals by type of service. Voluntary health insurance—with the exception of the group-practice prepayment plans, which cover less than 5 per cent of the population—is concerned mainly with hospital and in-hospital services. These would include hospital care, surgery, and obstetrics. The percentages of all charges for those services covered by insurance, comprising insured and uninsured persons are shown in Table 4.

Table 4*

Type of service	Per cent of charges covered by insurance
Hospital	50
Surgery	38
Obstetrics	25

* Detailed data can be found in Table A-14.

For all physicians' charges the percentage covered by insurance is 13 per cent; the percentage covered by insurance for nonsurgical and nonobstetric services is 4 per cent. The percentage covered for other services such as dentistry, medicines, and other medical goods and services is negligible or nonexistent, because it is not current insurance practice, with few exceptions, to cover those services.

NATIONWIDE CHARGES FOR PERSONAL HEALTH SERVICES AND THE FAMILY

The family is the logical unit for discussing the charges for personal health services, because it is an earning, spending, and consuming unit in our society. In considering spendable income, the source of income is the main earner in a family unit, and subsidiary units such as a working wife and partially or wholly self-supporting dependents living at home.

On a national basis the $10.2 billion charged for private personal health services becomes $207 per family. It is more comprehensible, however, to use the median charges of $110, indicating that one-half of the families incur charges of less than $110 and one-half incur charges in excess of $110. The average or mean is higher than the median, because extremely high costs among relatively few families pull the mean up and make it difficult to determine the distribution of charges.

The median charges by family income are shown in Fig. 7. The higher the income, the greater is the amount of incurred charges for personal health services. This is not simply because the upper-income groups utilize more services; they are also likely to be charged more, and to occupy more expensive hospital rooms than lower-income groups.

At this point it is well to note the apparent impact that health insurance has on the over-all costs of personal health services. It was noted in Fig. 7 that families with insurance incur median charges of $145 and those without insurance $63. It is obvious that, on the basis

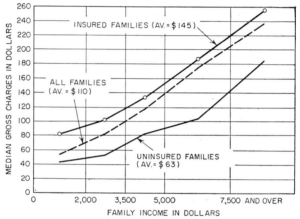

Fig. 7. Median gross charges incurred per family for all personal health services, by family income and insurance status (see Table A-15).

of the median, families with insurance incur charges exceeding twice that of uninsured families. If the amount paid by insurance is deleted, leaving out-of-pocket expenses of $117, this is still twice the charges incurred by uninsured families. In using the mean it is found that out-of-pocket charges incurred by insured families total $192 (inclusion of insurance benefits makes the total $237), which is still higher than the charges incurred by uninsured families, namely, $154. It will also be noted that these differences hold for each income group, although not necessarily in the same proportions from income group to income group.

It is thus obvious that families with insurance not only incur total charges appreciably higher than uninsured families, but they also

incur higher charges for uninsured services. In the utilization data it
will be shown that insured families receive more services, but they
incur higher out-of-pocket charges.

All families incur charges slightly in excess of a median of 4.1 per
cent and a mean of 4.6 per cent of their annual incomes. Continuing
with the median, the lower the income group, the higher is the median
percentage of income incurred for costs of personal health services.
It is also apparent that insured families have a median cost 40 per
cent greater than uninsured families. It is interesting to note, however,
that among uninsured families the lowest- and highest-income groups

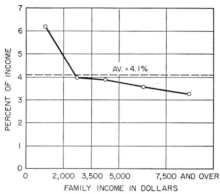

Fig. 8. Median percentage of family income paid out for personal health services
and for voluntary health insurance, by family income under $10,000 (see Table
A-16).

have the greatest median percentage of family income going for
personal health services (see Table A-16).

As measured by percentage of family income, it is apparent that
charges for personal health services represent a relatively small part
of a family's total family budget. In a later chapter the distribution of
the charges will be presented, indicating that there is a considerable
variation in the percentage of family income incurred for costs of
personal health services among all families in a year.

It was stated previously that American families incurred charges of
$207 per year per family. When this total is broken down by type of
service, families incur charges for each service as shown in Table 5.

The mean charges per family by type of service would be the same
as the percentage breakdown of the medical dollar on a national basis

Table 5

Type of service	Mean charges incurred per family
All Services..................	$207
Physicians..................	78
Hospitals..................	41
Medicines..................	31
Other..................	26
Dentists..................	33

as in Fig. 6. The data in Table 5 show what each type of service amounts to, in terms of dollars.

There is a common assumption that health-care charges in urban areas are higher than in rural areas of the country. This assumption is borne out in Table 6, since families living in metropolitan areas incur charges of $237 per family and those in rural areas $178. Among families with gross charges the means are $259 and $190 respectively.

Table 6

Residence	Mean gross charges per family	Mean gross charges per family with gross charges
All families..................	$207	$225
Urban areas of 1 million or more.	237	259
Other urban..................	204	221
Rural nonfarm..................	193	212
Rural farm..................	178	190

The differences are largely reflections of higher unit costs, since utilization of services in rural areas for most services usually equals or exceeds that of urban areas. The most startling difference in costs is found in dentistry. The families in metropolitan areas average $51 a year and rural farm families $19. In this type of service, however, higher utilization in metropolitan areas accounts more for this difference than unit cost of dental services. The steadiest service in terms of charges among all families regardless of residence is medicines. The average charge per family varies between $29 and $33, a narrow range.

A review of Tables A-18 to A-24 will reveal appreciable differences in charges incurred by insured and uninsured families regardless of residence, insured families incurring considerably higher charges than uninsured families. It is worth noting, however, that the impact of insurance on hospital costs is greater among insured rural farm families than in any other locality. The same appears to be true for physicians' costs among families in metropolitan areas.

It will be recalled that in the early part of this chapter the composition of the medical dollar on a national basis by type of service was presented. Approximately 57 per cent of the medical dollar was allocated to hospital and physicians' services. Do the proportions among services in the medical dollar differ between income groups or between those insured and uninsured? It might be assumed that the lower the income group the higher is the proportion of the medical dollar going for hospital and physicians' services. On examination, however, hospital and physicians' costs remain quite constant among various income groups, but the proportions spent for medicines and dentistry vary considerably. Fifty-nine per cent of the medical dollar in the lowest-income group goes for hospital and physicians' services and 55 per cent in the highest-income group. The lowest-income group spends proportionately more for medicines than does the highest-income group and proportionately less for dental care (see Table A-25).

Comparisons between insured and uninsured persons reveal that hospital and physicians' charges account for 59 and 56 per cent of the medical dollar respectively, a minor difference (see Table A-26). Comparisons by income groups do reveal, however, that insured lower-income families spend more of the medical dollar for hospital and physicians' services than other income groups, insured or uninsured.

NATIONWIDE CHARGES FOR PERSONAL HEALTH SERVICES AND THE INDIVIDUAL

Although, for certain purposes, the family is the logical unit for discussing costs of personal health services, it is also necessary to present costs for individuals as well, since there are considerable variations by age and sex. In fact, age and sex are the basic variables for estimating costs and utilization of personal health services, as will be noted in the data to follow.

The charges per person per year for all personal health services

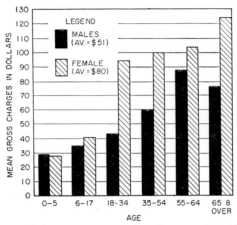

Fig. 9. Mean gross total charges per person for all personal health services, by age and sex (see Table A-27, footnote regarding dip in charges).

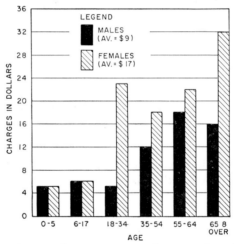

Fig. 10. Mean gross hospital charges per person, by age and sex (see Table A-28).

total $65. It will be recalled that the charges per family were $207. The charges for males totaled $51 and for females $80, a common pattern. The higher the age, the greater were the charges incurred for all services. Also, except in the age group under 5, females incurred greater charges in all age groups than males. The mean per capita charges by type of service and by sex are noted in Figs. 10 to 14. In all instances the female incurs higher charges than the male. Com-

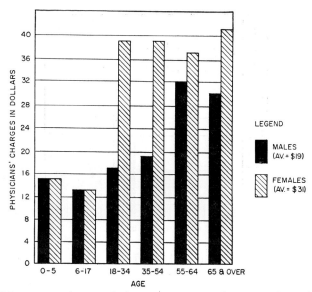

Fig. 11. Mean gross physicians' charges per person, by age and sex (see Table A-29).

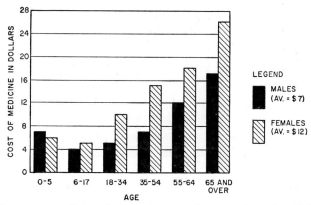

Fig. 12. Mean gross medicine charges per person, by age and sex (see Table A-30).

parisons by age groups, however, show that charges for females are not appreciably higher than charges for males until after age 17.

When per capita charges are classified by insured and uninsured persons, it is found that persons with insurance incurred gross charges of $74 and those without insurance $55. A further breakdown by age and sex reveals that insured persons generally incur higher charges

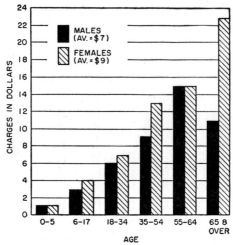

Fig. 13. Mean gross "other" medical charges per person, by age and sex (see Table A-31).

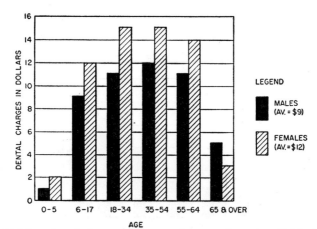

Fig. 14. Mean dental charges per person, by sex and age (see Table A-32).

than the uninsured. In analyzing the financial impact of insurance, it is interesting to note that insurance appears to have a diminishing effect on costs as age rises or an increasing effect on costs in the younger age groups, as noted in Table 7.

For both sexes it will be noted that the age group under 5 with insurance incurred charges 75 per cent higher than the same age group without insurance. At the other end of the life span, the age

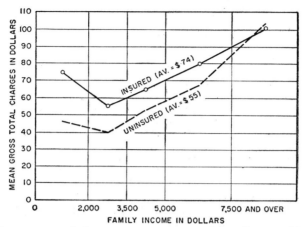

Fig. 15. Mean gross total charges per person incurred for all personal health services, by family income and insurance status (see Table A-33).

Table 7. Percentage Excess in Charges of Insured Persons over Uninsured Persons for All Personal Health Services by Age

Age	Both sexes, %	Male, %	Female, %
All ages.............	35	54	26
Under 6...........	75	100	45
6–17..............	100	91	96
18–34.............	65	107	41
35–54.............	35	60	26
55–64.............	25	59	8
65 and over........	13	−12*	41

*Minus excess.

group 65 and over with insurance incurred charges 13 per cent higher than those without insurance.

Since only hospital services and a small part of physicians' services are insured to any substantial degree, it is well to break down the differences in cost for these services by age and sex. It is found, as in Table 8, that insured persons incur hospital charges 78 per cent higher than those without insurance. For physicians' services, it is found that insured persons incur charges 33 per cent higher than uninsured persons. With advancing age the difference diminishes.

A breakdown of the mean gross charges per person by family in-

Table 8. Percentage Excess in Charges of Insured Over Uninsured Persons for Hospital and Physicians' Services by Age

Age	Hospital services, %	Physicians, %
All ages..........	78	33
Under 6.........	200	64
6–17.............	350	78
18–34............	111	67
35–54............	55	28
55–64............	60	9
65 and over.......	41	0

come reveals, as in charges per family, that the higher the income the higher are the incurred charges. Among all income groups except the highest, or $7,500 and over, the insured individual incurs higher charges than the uninsured individual. This would seem to indicate

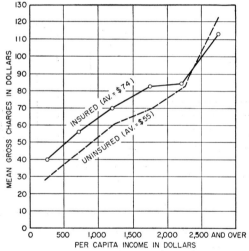

Fig. 16. Mean gross charges per person incurred for all personal health services, by per capita income and insurance status (see Table A-34).

that, after family income is over $7,500, families tend to spend the same amounts for personal health services regardless of whether or not they have insurance.

As a summary of this chapter, a few selected over-all figures may be presented in order to give a general view of the charges for personal health services on a national basis. Various segments of the population account for varying proportions of the $10.2 billion incurred for personal health services in a year. Selected segments are as follows:

1. The age group under 6 comprises 13 per cent of the population and incurs 6 per cent of all charges for personal health services.
2. The age group under 18 comprises 34 per cent of the population and incurs 18 per cent of all charges.
3. The age group 55 and over comprises 17 per cent of the population and incurs 26 per cent of all charges.
4. The age group 65 and over comprises 9 per cent of the population and incurs 13 per cent of all charges.
5. Females comprise 52 per cent of the population and incur 63 per cent of all charges.
6. Females in the childbearing ages from 18 to 44 comprise 20 per cent of the population and incur 28 per cent of all charges.
7. Families with incomes of $5,000 and over comprise 32 per cent of the population and incur 46 per cent of all charges.

5

Distribution of Charges
for Personal Health Services
among Families and Individuals

FAMILIES

Gross Distributions

It will be recalled that the total nationwide charges for private personal health services is $10.2 billion, which in turn averages $207 a family. It would appear that $207 per family, or approximately 4 to 5 per cent of the family income, would not in the great majority of families be an excessive expenditure to bear during a year. If all families could be assured that their annual costs would never exceed 4 to 5 per cent of their incomes, there would be no particular problem. As someone aptly said, "It's not the cost; it's the uncertainty" which is the problem. The fact that all the nation's families incur charges of $10.2 billion is not the issue—perhaps the total should be $8 billion or $15 billion if a scientific standard could be established—the issue is the uneven distribution of costs among families during the year.

In Fig. 17 it can be seen that in one year 8 per cent of the families incurred no charges at all for personal health services, and 2 per cent of the families incurred charges in excess of approximately $1,000. Thus 2 per cent of the families, or approximately one million families, incurred close to 16 per cent of the total charges for personal health services. Another way to state this is that 46 per cent of the families incurred charges under approximately $100[1] or none at all, accounting for 7.5 per cent of the total charges for personal health services. On

[1] For simplicity of presentation, figures of $95 or $195, etc., will be rounded out to $100 and $200.

the other end of the distribution, approximately 11 per cent of the families incurred charges in excess of approximately $500, accounting for 43 per cent of the total charges.

The fact that medical costs are unevenly distributed among families comes as no surprise to students of medical economics. The study of the Committee on the Costs of Medical Care established this fact con-

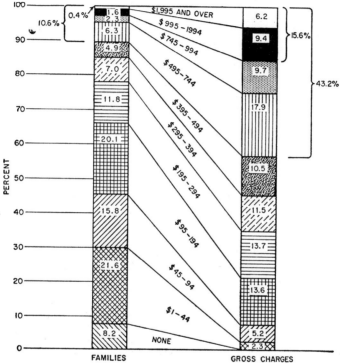

Fig. 17. Percentage distribution of families and total gross charges, by family total gross charges groupings (see Table A-35).

clusively. The cost distributions in the present survey confirm the previous findings and provide current data applicable to present-day conditions. It is interesting to note, however, that the CCMC study reported that 10 per cent of the families incurred 41 per cent of the charges in a year, coming amazingly close to the parallel percentages of 11 per cent and 43 per cent in the present survey.[2]

[2] I. S. Falk, Margaret C. Klem, and Nathan Sinai, *The Incidence of Illness and the Receipt and Costs of Medical Care among Representative Families: Experiences in Twelve Consecutive Months during 1928–1931*, Chicago, University of Chicago Press, 1933, p. 211 (publication of the CCMC, no. 26).

A final remark on the distribution of charges for personal health services among families is directed to a presentation of the family outlay for all personal health services as a percentage of family income. It will be seen in Fig. 18 that 5 per cent of the families made no outlay of any kind. The outlay of an additional 53 per cent of the families was under 5 per cent of their incomes. On the other end, it is noted that 7 per cent of the families incurred charges exceeding 20 per cent of their incomes—among them, 2 per cent who incurred charges exceeding 50 per cent of their incomes.[3] The median was 4.1 per cent,

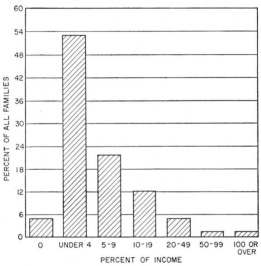

Fig. 18. Outlay for all personal health services and for voluntary health insurance as a percentage of family income (see Table A-36).

meaning that half the families incurred charges exceeding 4.1 per cent of their incomes and half the families incurred charges less than 4.1 per cent of their incomes.

Gross Distribution by Type of Service

For purposes of calculating costs, personal health services can be classified by type of service and the distribution of costs of such services among families. For the most part, current health-insurance plans and policies are written in terms of types of service. It is assumed that some types of services lend themselves more readily to

[3] See Table A-37 for discussion of characteristics of families with large percentages of their incomes incurred for costs of medical care.

insurance than others and may also be a greater drain on family financial resources at any one time.

There is a great deal of variation in the distribution of costs between types of services. As might be expected, families are much more likely to incur physicians' costs in a year than hospital costs. Within physicians' costs, families are much less likely to incur costs for surgery than other physicians' services. Among families who incur costs for the various types of services there is also great variation between services as to the cost distributions of those services. For instance, 3 per cent of the families incurred charges for surgery of under $45, but 46 per cent of the families incurred charges for medicines under $45.

If a figure of $195 is chosen arbitrarily, what percentage of the families incur charges in excess of that figure, and for what type of service? Table 9 shows the percentage of families incurring charges in excess of $195 by type of service.

Table 9

Type of service	Per cent of families
All services	34
Surgery	3
"Other" physicians	6
Hospital	6
Medicines	2
"Other" services	2
Dental	4

Present-day health insurance is geared mainly to hospital care and in-hospital physicians' services because of the assumption that they constitute the sudden and high-cost services. Over a period of a year it is revealed that, for physicians' services other than surgery and obstetrics, 6 per cent of the families incur charges in excess of $195, and for surgery 3 per cent of the families incur charges in excess of a similar amount. Six per cent of the families incur charges in excess of $195 for hospital care. Thus, it is seen that multiples of small costs such as nonsurgical and nonobstetric physicians' services add up to substantial amounts and exceed that of surgery. Two per cent of the families incurred charges for medicines in excess of $195, 2 per cent for "other" medical goods and services, and 4 per cent for dental services. It may be a moot question as to whether these services can or should be covered by health insurance, but the fact remains that some families incur high costs for each type of service.

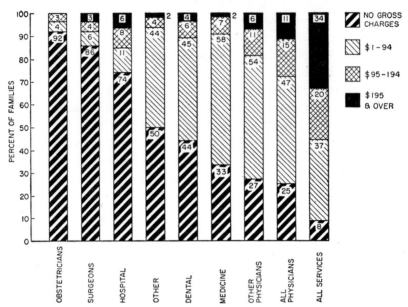

Fig. 19. Percentage distribution of gross charges for personal health services among families, by type of service (see Table A-38).

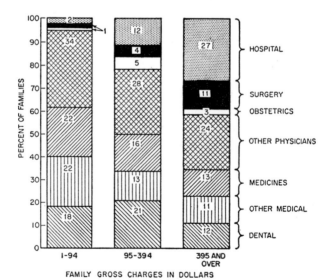

Fig. 20. Percentage distribution of gross total charges among families, by type of service and level of charges (see Table A-39).

It has been shown that certain percentages of families incurred total charges in excess of selected amounts such as $100, $200, and more. It was also noted that certain types of personal health services account for certain percentages of the entire medical dollar. As the incurred charges experienced by families increase, does the distribution of the percentages making up the medical dollar change, or does it remain quite constant? Reference to Fig. 20 will shed some light on this question.

It will be noted that, as the incurred charges increase, a greater percentage goes to the hospital and for surgery. In almost all instances the percentage of the other services decreases. This does not mean, of course, that the absolute amounts incurred for these other services are small.

Gross Distribution by Type of Service and Income of Family

When the distribution of incurred charges for personal health services is broken down by family income, it is noted that the higher the income the greater is the percentage of families incurring high charges. Likewise, the smaller the income the less likelihood there is of incurring any charges at all. This is an expected phenomenon, and there are several reasons for it, which cannot be separated in this study.

The higher the income the greater is the utilization of services, and the greater is the possibility of being charged more per unit of service, particularly physicians' services and to some extent hospital services, if relatively high-priced accommodations are utilized. Families with incomes over $7,500 are over three times more likely to incur charges in excess of $295 than families with incomes of $2,000 and less. Three per cent of families with incomes of $7,500 and over incurred no charges, and 16 per cent of families with incomes of $2,000 and under. An undetermined proportion of families in the latter income group received "free" services.

When incurred charges for personal health services are broken down by type of service and family income, it is again apparent that high income and relatively high charges are associated (Figs. 21 to 24). The families with incomes over $7,500 are over twice as likely to incur hospital charges in excess of $195 as families with incomes under $2,000. Other services run as follows: (1) all physicians' services, four times greater; (2) surgical services, five times greater; (3) "other" physicians' services, almost four times greater; (4) medicines, twice

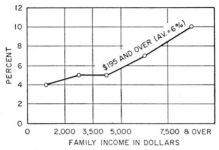

Fig. 21. Percentage distribution of gross hospital charges exceeding $195 among families, by family income (see Table A-40).

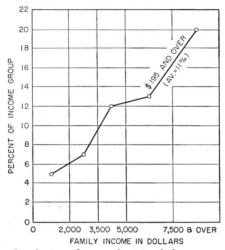

Fig. 22. Percentage distribution of gross physicians' charges exceeding $195 among families, by family income (see Table A-41).

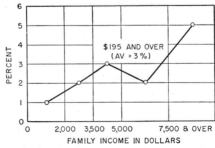

Fig. 23. Percentage distribution of gross surgical charges exceeding $195 among families, by family income (see Table A-42).

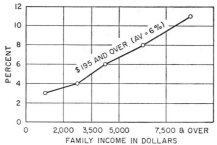

Fig. 24. Percentage distribution of gross "other" physicians' charges exceeding $195 among families, by family income (see Table A-44).

as great; (5) "other" services, three times greater; and (6) dental services, ten times greater (see Tables A-40 to A-47).

Gross Distributions by Type of Service and Residence

In the foregoing chapter it was indicated that rural farm families on an average incurred lower charges for personal health services than urban families. An examination of Tables A-48 to A-51 will reveal, however, that the proportion of families with relatively high charges such as $195 and over are quite constant by type of residence. By type of residence the proportion of families who incur charges of $195 or more for all services is as shown in Table 10. By selected services the

Table 10

Residence	Per cent of families incurring charges of $195 and over
Urban, areas of 1 million or more	36
Other urban	34
Rural nonfarm	30
Rural farm	32

proportion of families who incur charges in excess of $195 is as shown in Table 11.

Table 11

Residence	Per cent of families incurring charges of $195 and over		
	Hospital	Physicians	Medicines
Urban, areas of 1 million or more	6	12	2
Other urban	6	10	2
Rural nonfarm	6	11	3
Rural farm	5	9	1

It should thus be clear that if health insurance is designed to cushion the relatively high costs incurred by a small percentage of families in a year, the problem is quite similar regardless of type of residence. It might also be argued that charges in excess of $195 in rural areas have a greater impact on family finances than in urban areas because family incomes are somewhat lower in rural areas than in urban areas.

INDIVIDUALS

With advancing age the proportion of individuals who incur relatively high charges increases. As Fig. 25 shows, 2 per cent of the individuals under 5 years of age and 13 per cent of the individuals over

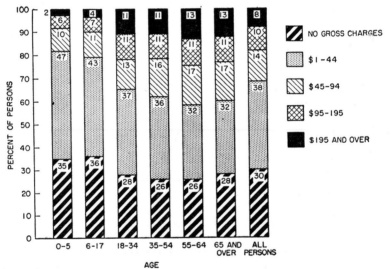

Fig. 25. Percentage distribution of persons by level of gross total charges for all personal health services, by age (see Table A-52).

55 years of age incur charges in excess of $195. The morbidity rate by age is relatively high in the young and older age groups and low in the middle, but apparently a relatively high morbidity rate in the young age group is not necessarily equated with a high cost of personal service because of the relative infrequency of hospital care and surgery. The age group under 5 is more likely to incur physicians' charges than age groups above it, but less likely to incur high charges.

The distribution of charges for surgery incurred by those who have surgery reveals that on a national basis approximately 27 per cent of the individuals with surgery incur charges in excess of $145, and 15 per cent in excess of $195. Thirty-three per cent incur charges under $45 (see Table A-55). The median surgical charges per individual is $69, and the mean is $101.

DEBT AMONG FAMILIES DUE TO COSTS OF PERSONAL HEALTH SERVICES

Being in debt is no novelty for the vast majority of American families, since they are accustomed to buying a wide range of goods on credit. In fact, "so much down and so much a month" is the mainstay of the automobile, refrigerator, radio and television, and furniture industries. Presumably, going into debt for automobiles, refrigerators, television sets, and many other items is pleasurable because one can "enjoy them while paying for them." There are also the factors of convenience of a payment plan and aggressive salesmanship.

Since being in debt is, so to speak, a normal experience for many American families, is there any cause for concern when one learns that 15 per cent of families are in debt to hospitals, physicians, dentists, and other providers of medical goods and services,[4] and that 2 per cent are in debt for $195 or more? Translated into absolute numbers, this means that approximately 7.5 million families in the United States have some medical debt and that about one million families owe $195 or more.

If personal health services could be purchased like any other goods or services—when desired, and in the quantity and of the quality to fit one's purse—perhaps the problem of medical debt could be dismissed as of no more concern that the balance owed by a family on its automobile or television set. The cost of these items is known in advance; the costs of personal health services are not so known, and when they are needed the consumer usually has no choice but to seek the necessary services, regardless of the cost, even if it means going into debt. Systematic saving is only a partial solution, since families would not know how much should be saved annually.

Earlier in this chapter, the distribution of the costs of personal health services by family income was presented, showing that some families incurred no costs during the survey year and some incurred

[4] Hereafter referred to as medical indebtedness.

costs equaling or exceeding their annual incomes. In the data to follow, showing the distribution of outstanding medical indebtedness, it
will be noted that such indebtedness is considerably less than the incurred charges presented in a previous chapter. Apparently, many of
the bills were paid by insurance and savings, but a residue of unpaid
bills remains. Considering the magnitudes of some of the incurred
charges, it is surprising that the residue of unpaid bills is actually as
small as indicated in this survey. Given the definition of medical indebtedness in the study, it would seem that such indebtedness excludes minor costs and includes only indebtedness which represents
some degree of hardship to the families.

Outstanding medical indebtedness includes debts owed to hospitals,
physicians, dentists, and other suppliers of medical goods and services
at the end of the survey year *less* any amount which the family
planned to pay on such bills during the month following the interview; that is, the informant was asked how much the family owed
for personal health services (including amounts owed on bills not yet
received) and was then asked how much the family planned to pay on
these bills during the next month. If the informant reported that the
family's only outstanding debt was $10 to the doctor and that the bill
would be paid during the next month, the family was recorded as having no outstanding indebtedness for personal health services.

This method of getting at outstanding indebtedness was used to
determine the number of families who were not current with respect
to debts for personal health services, i.e., the number of families who
had owed hospitals, physicians, and others for a period longer than
"normal" interim between receiving services or goods and paying for
them. The amount of outstanding indebtedness then included all such
debts, whether incurred prior to the survey year or during the survey
year, except that the amount which the family planned to pay in the
month following the interview was excluded.

An important point to bear in mind is that medical indebtedness
excludes debts to financial institutions and individuals which were
incurred to pay for personal health services and goods.

All families in this survey showed 85 per cent with no medical indebtedness and 15 per cent with some debt. The 15 per cent with
some debt includes 9 per cent under $94, 3 per cent $95 to $194, 2 per
cent $195 and over, and 1 per cent where the amount was unknown.
The mean debt per family with medical indebtedness is $121. In na-

tional terms, this means that total indebtedness approximates $900 million (see Tables A-56 to A-60).

The percentage of all families with some medical indebtedness is quite constant until the income groups $5,000 and over are reached. Thereafter, there is a sharp drop. This is not a surprising fact, of course, since upper-income groups lay out a smaller percentage of their income for personal health services, although their average family costs are higher. It is also of particular interest to note that having or not having insurance had no real appreciable effect on indebtedness. A final observation is that indebtedness in families with incomes under $2,000 undoubtedly represents a greater burden than indebtedness in income groups with higher incomes. Debts are not necessarily distributed evenly in proportion to incomes, as is shown in the tables.

The lowest-income group has the highest percentage of families with medical debt under $95, namely, 13 per cent; 4 per cent of the highest-income group has debts of similar magnitude. It would appear that, in three of the income groups, those with insurance are more likely to have debts under $95 than those without insurance.

For families with medical debts ranging from $95 to $194 again, the lower the income group the greater is the hardship experienced. The effect of insurance is negligible, although more care is received.

There is an interesting uniformity of percentage of families with medical debts exceeding $195, 2 per cent, but the lower the income group the greater is the hardship involved on the part of the families.

Other tables in Appendix A show anticipated patterns and help to buttress the data on medical indebtedness presented in the foregoing data. By and large, the greater the percentage of family income paid out for personal health services, the larger is the proportion of families who reported outstanding medical indebtedness. This is also true within income groups as well as between income groups.

Finally, families with children are more likely to report medical indebtedness than families without children. This is another way of saying that increased financial responsibilities are incurred in families with children and that medical indebtedness is distributed unevenly among families (see Tables A-61 to A-65).

CHAPTER 6   *Health Insurance and the*
Charges for Personal
Health Services

In foregoing chapters it has been shown that families and individuals with insurance incurred greater charges for personal health services than did families and individuals without insurance. Possible reasons for this difference have already been discussed. Among families and individuals with insurance, what proportions of the charges incurred for personal health services were covered by insurance? Such data provide some indication of the adequacy of voluntary health insurance in spreading the cost of personal health services.

HEALTH-INSURANCE BENEFITS
AND GROSS CHARGES INCURRED

All families with some type of health insurance had 19 per cent of their gross total charges for all personal health services paid by insurance. This is not to imply that the other 81 per cent of the charges for personal health services should be covered by insurance. As was stated earlier, the most comprehensive health-insurance plans in this country hardly cover 50 per cent of the costs of all services in a year. Later in this chapter, data on the extent to which insurance covered costs of services will be presented by type of service, but for the moment charges for all services will be discussed.

In Fig. 26 it is revealed that the higher the charges incurred by families with insurance the greater was the percentage of those charges covered by insurance up to approximately $400. Thereafter the percentage stabilized at 23 to 25 per cent no matter how high the total charges, at least in the magnitudes possible in this survey. It is noted that as charges reach magnitudes which can be recognized as "catastrophic," for which current major-medical contracts are designed, present-day health insurance has a diminishing effect. It is unlikely that the exclusion of dental services, appliances, and some other types of services would have an appreciable effect in raising the percentage of charges paid by insurance, because these services diminish in importance as a percentage of total charges with the increase in total charges (see Table A-39).

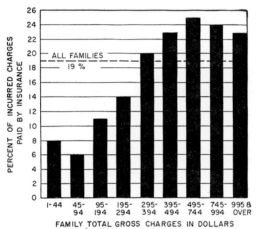

Fig. 26. Total insurance benefits as a percentage of total gross charges for insured families, by their total gross charges (see Table A-66).

Each insured family received as an average $45 in health-insurance benefits, this average ranging from $2 to $362 depending on the size of the incurred charges. Insured families who actually received benefits received as an average $144, this average ranging from $20 to $490 (see Tables A-66 to A-67).

The average insurance benefit received by all insured individuals was $17; for individuals receiving benefits it was $116. With advancing age the benefits increased, indicating increased utilization at least as measured by costs (see Table A-68).

A more meaningful method of measuring the extent to which present-day health insurance meets high charges incurred by families is to determine what percentage of insured families with charges in excess of approximately $500 have given percentages of their charges paid by insurance. The following data set this forth (see detailed Table A-69):

1. 27 per cent of the families had 40 per cent or more of their charges paid by insurance.
2. 19 per cent of the families had 50 per cent or more of their charges paid by insurance.
3. 10 per cent of the families had 60 per cent or more of their charges paid by insurance.
4. 2 per cent of the families had 80 per cent or more of their charges paid by insurance.

To pinpoint the impact of insurance benefits a little more, the following data set forth the percentages of insured families who incurred charges in excess of $500 and also received benefits (since some insured families incurred charges and received no benefits):

1. 38 per cent of the families had 40 per cent or more of their charges paid by insurance.
2. 27 per cent of the families had 50 per cent or more of their charges paid by insurance.
3. 15 per cent of the families had 60 per cent or more of their charges paid by insurance.
4. 2.4 per cent of the families had 80 per cent or more of their charges paid by insurance.

HEALTH-INSURANCE BENEFITS AND GROSS CHARGES INCURRED BY INCOME

In general all insured families had 19 per cent of all their charges for personal health services met by insurance. When the figures are broken down by family income, it is noted that the lower the income of families with insurance the higher was the proportion of total charges met by insurance.

At first sight it may seem that insurance carried by low-income families was more "adequate" than that carried by upper-income families. Actually, low-income families are less likely to utilize and incur charges for services other than hospital care and surgery, the services most likely not to be covered by insurance among insured families. Thus in the aggregate, insurance among low-income families covers a

Table 12

Family income	Per cent of charges met by insurance	
	All insured families	Families receiving benefits
All incomes............	19	35
Under $2,000..........	26	52
$2,000–$3,499..........	20	38
3,500– 4,999..........	22	37
5,000– 7,499..........	18	32
7,500 and over........	15	30

higher proportion of total charges than among upper-income families. In all likelihood, upper-income families carry insurance with greater benefits than lower-income families, but such benefits are not reflected in total charges for all services among upper-income families. If the charges for hospital care and surgery were isolated, it is possible that benefits received among upper-income families would cover a greater proportion of charges than among lower-income families. This may not turn out to be so, since low-income families are more likely to use relatively low-cost services such as a ward in a hospital or be billed at a lower fee for surgery. It is clear that standards of adequacy of insurance benefits are extremely difficult to establish.

When the percentage of total costs met by insurance is isolated for persons, instead of for families, and is broken down by family income, it is again noted that the lower the income the greater is the percentage of charges among insured individuals met by insurance.

Table 13

Family income	Per cent of charges met by insurance
All incomes...........................	23
Under $2,000...........................	33
$2,000–$3,499...........................	23
3,000– 4,999...........................	26
5,000– 7,499...........................	21
7,500 and over...........................	18

Insured individuals have a slightly higher proportion of their charges covered by insurance than insured families, because among insured families there is a small proportion of individuals who have no insurance, thereby reducing the percentage of charges covered by insurance in comparison with insured individuals.

PROPORTIONS OF CHARGES MET BY INSURANCE BY TYPE OF SERVICE

For all services, 21 per cent of the families received some service for which insurance was paid in whole or in part (see Table A-73). For 29 per cent of the families who received insurance benefits, 20

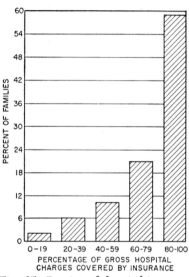

Fig. 27. Receipt of hospital-insurance benefits to cover gross hospital charges (see Table A-75).

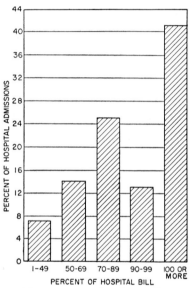

Fig. 28. Percentage distribution by percentage of hospital charges covered by insurance for admissions where some hospital benefits were received (see Table A-76).

per cent or less of their charges for services was paid by insurance. On the other end, 7 per cent of the families received insurance to cover 80 per cent or more of their charges.

Again, these gross figures for all services are more meaningful when they are broken down by specific types of services since, on a nationwide basis, voluntary health insurance almost always covers hospital care, surgery, and obstetrical care. Other services are covered only in isolated instances.

For hospital service, 59 per cent of the families experiencing hospital charges and receiving insurance benefits had 80 per cent or more of their costs covered (Fig. 27). On the other end, 18 per cent of the families had less than 60 per cent of their hospital charges covered by insurance. It is well to remember that these are national figures, and there are undoubtedly regional variations and variations among hospital-insurance plans.

A refinement in showing degree to which hospital insurance covers costs of hospital care is one of a breakdown by hospital admission where some benefits were received instead of by families receiving hospital care and insurance benefits. This method then shows (Fig. 28) that 54 per cent of the hospital admissions receiving insurance benefits had 90 per cent or more of hospital charges paid by insurance. Approximately 41 per cent had the entire charges paid.

The next type of service for which a great deal of insurance is written is surgery. Thirty-four per cent of the insured families who experience surgical charges have less than 60 per cent of their charges covered by insurance, and 45 per cent have 80 per cent or more of such charges covered (Fig. 29).

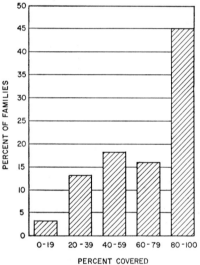

Fig. 29. Receipt of surgical or medical insurance benefits to cover gross surgical charges (see Table A-77).

The simple fact appears to be that by and large the payments made by insurance for surgical charges fall short of equaling total charges. The difference would seem to involve more than a normal deductible or co-insurance feature. To what extent is the low proportion of charges covered by surgical insurance due to low fee schedules established by insurance in relation to prevailing surgical fees? On the other hand, to what extent does surgical insurance tend to increase the per-unit surgical charges?

In order to pinpoint the impact of hospital and surgical insurance on families who experienced charges for the two services simultaneously and also received insurance benefits, families were isolated who had those experiences. Data are presented in Table 14 (see Table A-80 for details). It is thus seen that in instances where families car-

Table 14

Mean gross total charges for all services............................... $528
Per cent of gross hospital charges covered by insurance.................. 76
Per cent of gross surgical charges covered by insurance.................. 60
Per cent of total gross hospital and surgical charges covered by insurance..... 70
Per cent of total gross charges for all services covered by insurance........ 42

ried both hospital and surgical insurance and received benefits to cover hospital and surgical costs, approximately 70 per cent of the charges for those services were met by insurance.

The final type of service which is very widespread in health-insur-

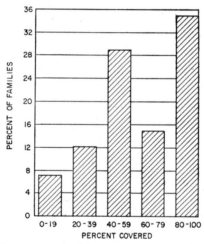

Fig. 30. Receipt of maternity benefits to cover gross obstetrical charges (see Table A-78).

ance contracts is maternity benefits. One-half of the maternity cases with insurance and receiving benefits had 60 per cent or more of the physicians' charges covered by insurance, and one-half had less than 60 per cent of charges covered (Fig. 30). Maternity benefits, however, are usually not designed to cover the total charges for maternity care. This may account, at least in part, for the relatively low proportion of obstetrical charges covered by maternity benefits.

⌈There has been a great increase in the utilization of personal health services in this country since 1940, among them hospitalization and surgery. Some of this increase has been attributed to the rise of voluntary health insurance and greater availability of facilities, and some to improved economic conditions for the great majority of families. An intangible element, but undoubtedly real, is greater consciousness of the value of these services among the general population. Certain it is, that the regard for and utilization of health services are part and parcel of a people's standard of living. ⟩

Insurance per se is associated with an increase in utilization, which is the chief reason why there is still debate as to whether personal health services are "insurable" or not. Fire insurance does not necessarily increase fires, nor does life insurance increase the death rate, but the introduction of health insurance is followed by an increase in the utilization of personal health services, as will be revealed in the data to follow. The need for health services is not so easily determined as the fact of a fire or the finality of death because no clear-cut criteria, except in gross instances, are available to determine need.

Although insurance is associated with an increase in utilization, it is an oversimplification to assert that insurance "causes" this increased utilization. ⌈The people who are more conscious of the value of personal health services may be more likely to avail themselves of health insurance than those who are not.⌉ Also people who know they need care in the near future may be likely to enroll in health insurance when it is made available, whether through employed group or individually. Group enrollment is not a perfect instrument to prevent adverse selection unless possibly a 100 per cent enrollment is required.

Whether this increase is good or bad can also be endlessly debated. Again, there are no standards, except very gross ones, of a "normal" hospital admission rate or a "normal" surgical rate. The rates emerge from the patterns of practice of thousands of physicians in their treatment of hundreds of thousands of patients. What was normal utilization 25 years ago is no longer normal utilization today, because so many factors have changed: buying power, new medical discoveries, and people's attitudes toward hospitals and other services.

A hospital-admission rate of 120 per 1,000 population today may be just as normal as a rate of 50 not so many years ago. Both emerge out of a combination of circumstances, the separate elements of which are almost impossible to disentangle. Whatever the utilization rate may be, it can be assumed that the nation, individually and collectively, is willing to pay the cost; otherwise insurance would not be so widespread and health facilities and personnel would not be in such great demand. Thus it can be said with certainty that the data to follow are a measure of effective demand.

HOSPITAL ADMISSIONS

By Age and Sex

The general hospital-admission rate for the country as a whole was 12 per 100 population per year. The admission rate for persons with hospital insurance was 14, and for those without such insurance, 9. On a national scale the difference between 14 and 9 is a rough measure of the influence of hospital insurance on hospital admissions today. It cannot be assumed, however, that the introduction of hospital insurance among those without such insurance could necessarily raise the admission rate from 9 to 14. Among both insured and uninsured persons the admission rate for females is appreciably higher than for males. Even with maternity cases excluded, the female rate is still slightly higher (Fig. 31).

Admissions for maternity comprise approximately 17 per cent of all hospital admissions. In the female age group 18 to 34, such admissions comprise 60 per cent of all admissions. In general the admission rate rises with age if admissions for maternity care are excluded. In all age groups those with hospital insurance have a higher admission rate than those without insurance.

When age groups are subdivided into their respective percentages of the total population and percentages of all hospital admissions, it is seen that age groups under 17 account for 33 per cent of the population but only 22 per cent of the hospital admissions. The age group from 18 to 34, on the other hand, accounts for 22 per cent of the popu-

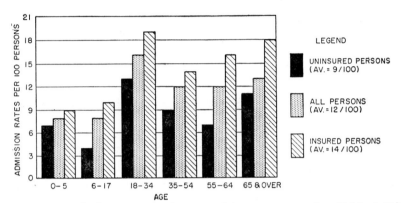

Fig. 31. Hospital-admission rates, by age and insurance status (see Table A-81).

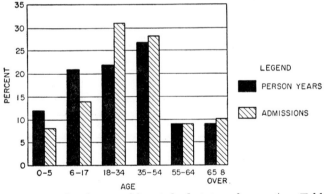

Fig. 32. Percentage distribution of hospital admissions, by age (see Table A-83).

lation but 31 per cent of the hospital admissions (Fig. 32). This is due largely to hospital admissions for maternity in this age group.

Those over 55 years of age account for 18 per cent of the population and 19 per cent of the hospital admissions. It was anticipated that a higher proportion in this age group than indicated would be hospitalized, but a more meaningful measure is one of number of hospital days by age, to be presented later.

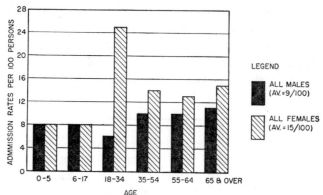

Fig. 33. Hospital-admission rates, by age and sex (see Table A-81).

By Family Income

For the general population, including both insured and uninsured persons, the hospital-admission rate varies very little between different income groups. In fact, the highest-income group shows indica-

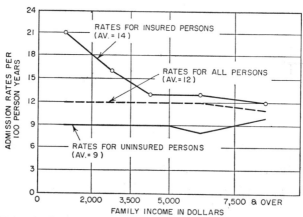

Fig. 34. Hospital-admission rates, by family income and insurance status (see Table A-84).

tions of having a lower admission rate than other income groups (Fig. 34).

A different picture emerges when hospital-admission rates between insured and uninsured individuals and by income groups are compared. Among insured individuals it can be stated that the lower the income the higher is the admission rate. Among uninsured individuals the highest-income group also has the highest admission rate but certainly not strikingly higher. Furthermore there is no progression by income group.

One thing is clear, however: insured persons, regardless of income, have an appreciably higher admission rate than uninsured persons. This is strikingly true for incomes under $3,500. Why this is so cannot be explained with any degree of conclusiveness in this survey. It is apparent that among low-income insured persons 55 years of age and over and with incomes under $2,000, the hospital-admission rate is over three times as great as among the parallel uninsured group.

It would appear that since 1933 the hospital-admission rate by family income has evened out, because in the data from the Committee on the Costs of Medical Care there is a clear progression between the hospital-admission rate and the family income, i.e., the higher the income the higher the admission rate, except for the lowest-income group.[1] In the present data it is evident that insurance has virtually

Table 15

CCMC data		Present survey data			
			Hospital admission rate per 1,000		
Family income	Hospital admission rate per 1,000	Family income	Total	Insured person	Uninsured person
Under $1,200.......	59	Under $2,000.....	120	210	90
$ 1,200-$ 2,000....	50	$2,000-$3,499....	120	160	90
2,000- 3,000....	58	3,500- 4,999....	120	130	90
3,000- 5,000....	63	5,000- 7,499....	120	130	80
5,000- 10,000....	75	7,500 and over...	110	120	100
10,000 and over...	106	Total..........	120	140	90
Total...........	59				

reversed the hospital-admission rate by family income; and it is further suggested that even among uninsured persons hospital care is regarded as being so important or made more easily accessible than formerly so that variations in admission rates between income groups are very slight. Data in Table 15 are illustrative.

[1] I. S. Falk, Margaret C. Klem, and Nathan Sinai, *The Incidence of Illness and the Receipt and Costs of Medical Care among Representative Families: Experiences in Twelve Consecutive Months during 1928–1931*, Chicago, University of Chicago Press, 1933, p. 113 (publication of the CCMC, no. 26).

By Residence

Traditionally, persons living in urban areas have had a higher hospital-admission rate than those living in rural areas. The study of the Committee on the Costs of Medical Care reported that in large urban areas the hospital admission rate was 71 per 1,000 population, and in small towns and rural areas the rate was 47.[2] The present survey reveals that the hospital-admission rates in urban and rural areas have reversed themselves during the past 20 years, so that now rural areas have a higher admission rate than urban areas (Fig. 35). This shift

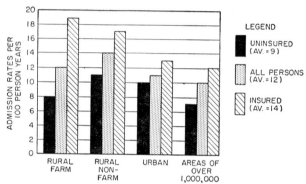

Fig. 35. Hospital-admission rates, by residence and insurance status (see Table A-85).

has apparently been brought about by insurance, since insured persons in rural areas have a much higher hospital-admission rate than insured persons in urban areas. Even among uninsured persons there is a tendency toward higher hospital-admission rates in rural areas than in other areas. It is clear from the foregoing that basic changes have taken place in rural medical practice over the past 20 years, with the hospital assuming an extremely important role in medical care. Additional evidence for this observation is available from the experience in the province of Saskatchewan, which has a provincewide hospital-insurance system. In Saskatchewan, rural areas have a higher hospital-admission rate than urban areas.[3]

[2] *Loc. cit.*

[3] Province of Saskatchewan, Saskatchewan Hospital Services Plan, *Annual Report, 1953*, Regina, Saskatchewan, Table XXII, p. 24.

LENGTH OF STAY

By Age and Sex

The mean length of stay for all hospital admissions was 7.4 days per admission. Persons with insurance had a shorter length of stay than those without insurance, 7 and 8.3 days respectively. Normally, one can expect a high admission rate to be associated with a relatively short length of stay and vice versa. This observation is borne out in comparing the insured and uninsured persons, since those with insur-

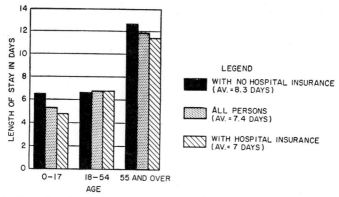

Fig. 36. Mean length of stay per admission, by age and insurance status (see Table A-86).

ance have a higher hospital-admission rate than those without (Fig. 36).

The higher the age the longer is the mean length of stay in hospitals. Also, males stay in a hospital longer than females (see Table A-86). Males and females with insurance have a shorter mean length of stay than males and females without insurance.

DISTRIBUTION BY LENGTH OF STAY

By Insurance Status

In 28 per cent of all hospital admissions, the persons admitted stayed only 1 or 2 days. In 19 per cent of the admissions, the persons stayed 10 or more days, and in 6 per cent the persons stayed 20 or more days. When admissions of persons with hospital insurance and without hospital insurance are compared, a greater percentage of the insured persons stay 1 or 2 days, and a smaller percentage stay 20 days or longer. It will be recalled that hospital-admission rates among insured persons are higher than among uninsured persons, probably indicating that insured persons on the whole are admitted to hospitals with less severe conditions requiring a shorter length of stay (Fig. 37).

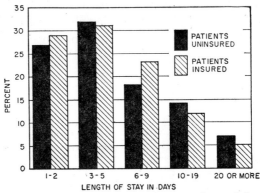

Fig. 37. Percentage distribution by length of stay in hospital for admissions, by insurance status (see Table A-87).

By Age and Sex

In Fig. 38 it is very clear that with advancing age a decreasing proportion of persons admitted stay 1 to 2 days, and an increasing propor-

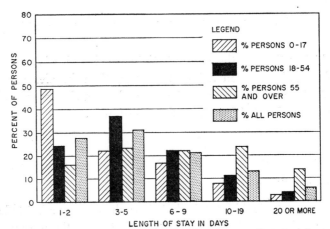

Fig. 38. Percentage distribution of length of stay per admission, by age (see Table A-87).

tion stay 10 to 20 days and longer. This certainly has a bearing on the age groups occupying hospital beds at a particular time and the kinds of illnesses under care.

An even more graphic method of showing the number of hospital days utilized by age is calculating the percentage of the total population made up by a given age group compared with its percentage of total hospital days utilized. In Fig. 39 it is revealed that the age group under 17 comprises 33 per cent of the population but utilizes only 16 per cent of all hospital days in a year. On the other end of the life

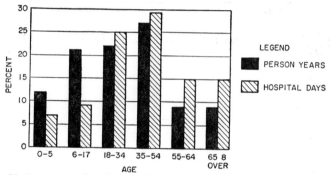

Fig. 39. Percentage distribution of hospital days, by age (see Table A-89).

span, those 55 years of age and over make up 18 per cent of the population but utilize 30 per cent of the hospital days. The presence or absence of insurance does not seem to have much effect on these ratios.

NUMBER OF HOSPITAL DAYS

By Age and Sex

The most meaningful measure of hospital utilization is the number of hospital days per person in a year. This measures the degree to which hospital beds are utilized and is an improvement over the admission rate.

In the general population there were 90 hospital days utilized per 100 persons. The rate for persons with insurance was 100, and for those without insurance, 70. A difference of 30 days reveals the in-

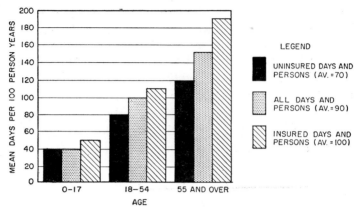

Fig. 40. Mean hospital days per 100 person-years, by age and insurance status (see Table A-88).

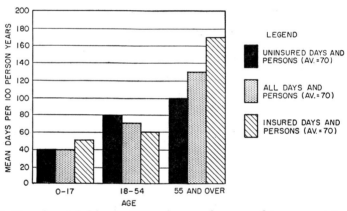

Fig. 41. Mean hospital days per 100 male-years, by age and insurance status (see Table A-88).

fluence that hospital insurance seems to have on hospital utilization (Fig. 40).

Apparently the increase in hospital days among the insured is attributable to increased female utilization, since insured and uninsured males both have a utilization rate of 70 days per 100 persons, and insured and uninsured females have a rate of 120 and 80 days per 100 persons respectively (see Table A-88).

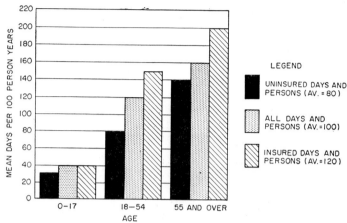

Fig. 42. Mean hospital days per 100 female-years, by age and insurance status (see Table A-88).

By Family Income

The number of hospital days per 100 persons by family income shows no consistent relationship for the general population. Among insured families, however, the lower the income the greater is the number of hospital days utilized. Among families without insurance the higher the income, the greater is the number of hospital days utilized, with the apparent exception of the lowest-income group (see Table A-90).

MISCELLANEOUS ITEMS

Hospitalized Deliveries

The mean number of hospital days for hospitalized deliveries was 4.7 days. Among all hospitalized deliveries, mothers with insurance stayed one day longer on an average than those without insurance, 5.1 and 4.0 days respectively. Fifteen per cent of all women hospitalized for deliveries were in the hospital from 1 to 2 days, while 28 per cent were hospitalized 6 days or more. Most of the women hospitalized for deliveries were in the hospital from 3 to 5 days. Insurance had an effect on length of stay by increasing the proportion of those who were hospitalized more than 6 days (see Table A-91).

Type of Accommodation

One of the important cost factors in hospital care is type of accommodation. Over the country the proportion of hospital admissions by

Table 16

Accommodation	Admissions, %
Private room	25
Semiprivate room	40
Ward	33
Undetermined	2

Table 17

Accommodation	Admissions without hospital insurance, %	Admissions with hospital insurance, %
Private room	26	24
Semiprivate room	30	45
Ward	41	29
Undetermined	3	2

type of accommodation is indicated in Table 16. Thus 25 per cent of the persons admitted occupy the most expensive accommodations, but most persons admitted occupy semiprivate rooms.

What effect does hospital insurance appear to have on type of accommodation? A review of the data in Table 17 indicates that insurance has the effect of increasing the proportion of patients occupying semiprivate accommodations and decreasing the proportion in ward accommodations. Apparently, there has been no effect on the proportion of persons admitted who occupy private rooms.

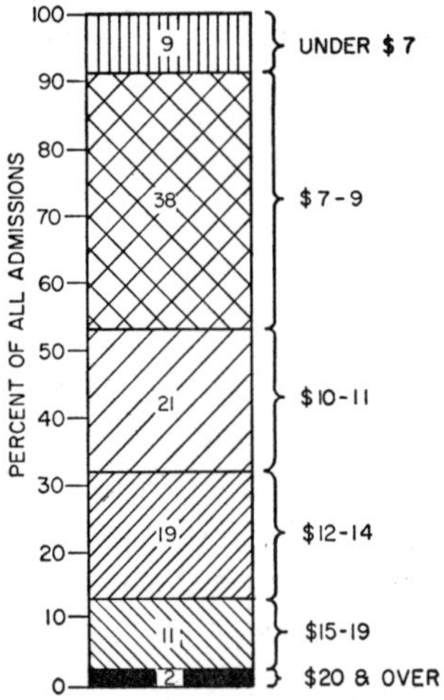

Fig. 43. Percentage distribution by daily room-and-board rates charged for admissions (see Table A-93).

Hospital Room-and-board Rates

Throughout the country, in 32 per cent of the hospital admissions, the patients occupied rooms costing $12 a day or more. The largest proportion, 38 per cent, occupied rooms costing between $7 and $10 a day. The patients with hospital insurance tended to occupy more expensive accommodations than those without insurance, since 46 per cent of the uninsured patients and 57 per cent of those insured occupied rooms costing more than $10 a day. This may not be entirely due to insurance, since most of the insured people live in urban areas, where hospital costs are higher than in rural areas (Fig. 43).

Type of Admission

Among all hospital admissions, the proportions of admissions by type of case were as follows:

Per cent

Obstetrics.......... 18
Surgery............ 38
Other............. 44

Among those with insurance there was an increase in the proportion of admission for surgery and medical services and a decrease for deliveries. This would indicate that insurance has a greater effect in increasing hospitalization for surgery and other medical conditions than for deliveries.

CHAPTER 8 *Utilization of Surgical and Other Services*

SURGICAL RATES BY AGE AND SEX

It has been shown that persons with hospital insurance utilize hospitals more frequently than persons without insurance. Likewise, it is found that persons with surgical insurance experienced more surgery than persons without such insurance. Persons covered by some type of surgical insurance had 9 surgical procedures per 100 persons as compared with 5 surgical procedures per 100 persons among persons with no surgical insurance, a very appreciable difference. By age, the differences between the insured and uninsured are marked until age 65 and over, at which point there appears to be very little difference (Fig. 44).

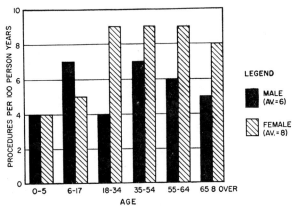

Fig. 44. Surgical procedures per 100 person-years, by age and sex (see Table A-94).

68

Up to age 65 there is a tendency for the number of surgical procedures to increase, but this trend is more apparent among females than males. It is also clear that, except for the age group 65 years of age and over, persons with surgical insurance are much more likely to undergo surgery than those without surgical insurance (Fig. 45).

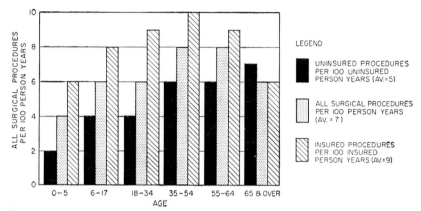

Fig. 45. Surgical procedures per 100 person-years, by age and insurance status (see Table A-94).

SURGICAL RATES BY INCOME

There is a clear relationship between family income and the surgical rate for both insured and uninsured individuals. In the case of the insured, the low-income groups under $3,500 experience a surgical rate much higher than the income groups over that income. Among uninsured individuals the surgical rate is lower for those under $3,500 than for those above that income.

An examination of Fig. 46 will show that persons with surgical insurance under $3,500 experienced surgery three to four times as often as persons without surgical insurance. It is of interest to note further that the persons in the three income groups over $3,500 with insurance also have more surgery than the persons in parallel income groups without insurance, but the differences between them are by no means as great as the differences between the insured and uninsured individuals under $3,500 described above.

Finally, it should be noted that there is no gradation in surgical rates by income among income groups $3,500 and over, whether insured or uninsured. Thus, it is apparent that the primary factor ac-

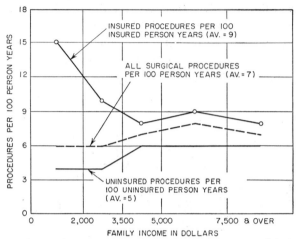

Fig. 46. Surgical procedures per 100 person-years, by income and insurance status (see Table A-95).

counting for the greater amount of surgery is the existence of insurance.

SURGICAL RATES BY RESIDENCE

No striking differences are found in the surgical rates by residence, since there is only a range of 6 to 7 surgical procedures per 100 population. With the presence of insurance, however, regardless of residence, persons with insurance have a consistently higher surgical rate than those without insurance. The startling find is that rural farm

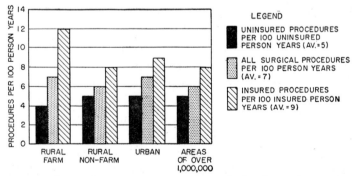

Fig. 47. Surgical procedures per 100 person-years, by locality and insurance status (see Table A-96).

residents with insurance have the highest surgical rate of any group. This follows the hospital-admission pattern, as will be recalled.

TYPES OF SURGICAL PROCEDURES

Because of the size of the sample it was not possible to break down the surgical procedures by type of operation. The sample was large enough, however, to permit a breakdown by tonsillectomies and appendectomies, two common types of operations. Table 18 shows dramatically the differences among the insured and uninsured persons. The tonsillectomy rate among insured children was more than three times that of uninsured children. For appendectomies, the insured persons had twice as many appendectomies as the uninsured persons.

Table 18. Selected Hospitalized-surgery Rates among Persons with and without Hospital Insurance at the Time of Admission for Surgery

Surgery	Rates per 1,000
Hospitalized tonsillectomies, children under 17	21
With hospital insurance	30
With no hospital insurance	9
Hospitalized appendectomies, persons 6–54	8
With hospital insurance	11
With no hospital insurance	5

What do the above surgical rates mean? Again, it is necessary to know more about the factors underlying the different rates. Very likely there is a higher proportion of so-called "elective" surgery among the insured persons, and a higher proportion of "emergency" or "must" surgery among the uninsured persons.

SURGICAL RATES NOW AND 25 YEARS AGO

A comparison of surgical rates brought out in the studies of the Committee on the Costs of Medical Care during the period from 1928 to 1931 and the present survey would appear to indicate that the over-all rate has increased little since those studies.[1] The Committee on the Costs of Medical Care study included suturing of wounds and circumcision, which were not classified as surgery in the present sur-

[1] Data from Selwyn D. Collins, "Frequency of Surgical Procedures among 9,000 Families Based on Nationwide Periodic Canvasses, 1928–31," *Public Health Reports,* **53:**587–628, Apr. 22, 1938.

vey. Even so, the exclusion of these procedures would reduce the over-all surgical rate by only a fraction of 1 per cent.

In any case, when rounded to the nearest decimal, the CCMC study shows a rate of 7 per 100 population and the present survey also shows a rate of 7. In both instances the female rate is greater than the male. Thus it would appear that the presence of surgical insurance has had no over-all effect in increasing surgery. Given this apparent fact, the explanation of the differences in surgical rates between insured and uninsured is by no means an obvious one.

The tonsillectomy rate in the United States during the CCMC study was much higher than in the present survey, a rate of 38 per 1,000 under 15 years of age compared with a rate of 21 per 1,000 under 17. The CCMC rate is also higher than that of the insured children in the present survey. Almost all tonsillectomies were performed in the hospital, since the total rate was 23 and the hospitalized rate was 21. Twenty-five years ago the rates were 38 and 28 respectively.

When surgical rates by family income are compared in the CCMC study and the current survey, it is found that the upper-income group had a rate almost twice as great as the lower-income group, 10 and 5 per 100 respectively. In the present survey it is clear that the difference between income groups has narrowed considerably, and now among the low-income insured population the surgical rate is even greater than among higher-income groups.

Another change that has taken place during the last 25 years is the disappearance of differences in surgical rates between rural and urban areas and among insured persons, literally a reversal of the previous pattern. In the CCMC survey the rural surgical rate was approximately 5 per 100 and the urban rate 8. In the present survey there is virtually no difference at all, and, as has been stated previously, in the case of the insured persons the rural surgical rate is distinctly higher than that of the urban. Even among the uninsured persons the differences are slight.

PHYSICIANS' CALLS

Because of the length of the reporting period, it was not possible to go into great detail on physicians' calls outside of the hospital. In any case it was possible to make reasonable estimates of the percentage of persons who had not consulted a physician once during the year and the percentage who had consulted a physician at least 15 times. It would seem that physicians' calls in excess of 15 would begin to represent a sizable total cost in a year, and it should be of interest to have some indication of the extent of that number of calls.

During the year 40 per cent of the people in the United States did not consult a physician. People with insurance were more likely to consult a physician than those without insurance, even though current health insurance does not generally cover out-of-hospital physicians' services. Thirty-six per cent of the insured persons did not see a physician compared with 45 per cent of the uninsured.

The age group most likely to require a physician's call was the age group under 6, and the age group least likely was the age group from 6 to 17 (Table 19). Females in every age group were more likely to consult a physician than males (see Table A-97).

Table 19. Per Cent with No Out-of-hospital Physicians' Calls

Age	Percentage
All ages	40
Under 6	28
6–17	48
18–34	37
35–54	41
55–64	42
65 and over	35

Seven per cent of the people consulted a physician at least 15 times during the year. It should be noted that the higher the age group (except under 6) the greater was the proportion of people who consulted a physician at least 15 times (Table 20).

Table 20. Estimated Per Cent with 15 or More Out-of-hospital Physicians' Calls

Age	Percentage
All ages	7
Under 6	3
6–17	2
18–34	6
35–54	8
55–64	12
65 and over	13

No standards are intended or implied in these data, since none have ever been agreed upon by any authoritative and responsible group.

It is sometimes suggested that everyone above age 40 should have an annual physical examination, but it is clear that around 45 per cent of the males above age 40 did not consult a physician for any reason, nor did around 35 per cent of the females.

OTHER SERVICES

In addition to data from the survey already discussed, information was available on dental services. In Fig. 48 it is clear that 34 per cent of the people in the United States consulted a dentist during the

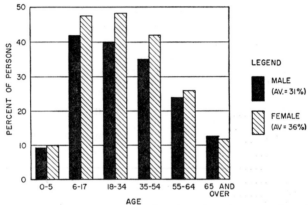

Fig. 48. Percentage of persons receiving dental services, by age and sex (see Table A-98).

12 months prior to the survey. If the advice of dentists had been followed to the full, 100 per cent of people 3 years of age and over should have consulted a dentist. Following previous studies, females were more likely to consult a dentist than males in all age groups except in the age group 65 and over.

Dental service by family income reveals that 17 per cent of the persons in the lowest-income group and 56 per cent in the highest-income group consulted a dentist (Fig. 49). It is thus apparent that even the highest-income group did not seek service in accordance with accepted dental standards, i.e., at least one visit a year. There is hardly a health service today which is so closely associated with income as dental service. Finally, persons with insurance were more likely to consult a dentist than persons without insurance regardless of income (see Table A-100).

A review of the CCMC data on dental service 25 years ago reveals that more people seek dental services today.[2] Approximately 26 per cent of the people consulted dentists 25 years ago compared with 34 per cent today. By age and sex the same pattern holds for both periods, although differing in magnitude, since the young and the old receive less service than the other age groups, and females receive more service than males.

It would appear that the lower-income groups are more likely to receive dental care today than 25 years ago, and upper-income groups receive about the same amount that they did at that time. Data from the CCMC survey show that in the lowest-income group approximately 12 per cent of the people sought dental care, and approximately 60 per cent of the people in the highest-income groups did. It is granted that perfect comparability between the two periods cannot

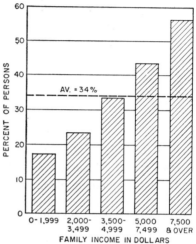

Fig. 49. Percentage of persons consulting dentists, by family income (see Table A-99).

be attained, but the data are certainly strongly suggestive of the above trends.

Finally, it was possible to determine what proportion of the people had received some kind of optical service, with no detail as to type of service. Fourteen per cent of the people had received some type of optical service during one year, increasing with age until age 65 and over. Females were more likely to receive optical care than males (see Table A-101).

[2] Selwyn D. Collins, "Frequency of Dental Services among 9,000 Families, Based on Nationwide Periodic Canvasses, 1928–31," *Public Health Reports,* **54:** 629–657, Apr. 21, 1939.

CHAPTER 9

Types of Insurers, Benefits, and Utilization of Services

In the foregoing data there has been no attempt to show how the various types of insurers—Blue Cross, Blue Shield, private companies, and the independent plans—compare as to proportion of charges for specified services covered and as to utilization of services on the part of their respective subscribers. Given the competitive nature of health insurance today and the fact that no single type of insurer dominates the field, such comparisons are in order. It should be emphasized, however, that comparisons brought out are true only for the time being. The field is changing rapidly enough so that a wholly different picture may emerge even a few years hence.

HOSPITAL CHARGES

It will be recalled that hospital insurance now pays approximately 50 per cent of the total private hospital charges in the United States. Thus insurance has had a greater impact on hospital services than on any other personal health service.

The two major types of insurers for hospital services are Blue Cross and private insurance companies. In Figs. 51 and 52 it is noted that Blue Cross and private insurance companies cover approximately the same proportion of the hospital charges in their group enrollment. In individual or nongroup enrollment, it appears that Blue Cross covers a larger proportion of the hospital charges.

The above comparisons take into consideration benefits only. No attempt has been made to compare benefits of Blue Cross and private

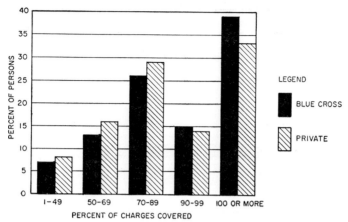

Fig. 50. Percentage distribution of admissions by percentage of hospital charges covered by insurance where some hospital insurance benefits were received, by type of insurance carrier (see Table A-102).

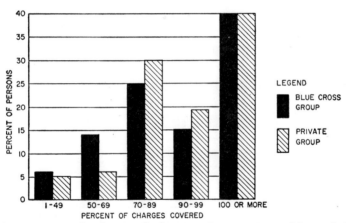

Fig. 51. Percentage distribution of admissions by percentage of hospital charges covered by insurance where some hospital insurance benefits were received, by type of insurance carrier and group enrollment (see Table A-102).

insurance companies in relation to their respective premiums. One important comparison was made, however, which indicates the role both types of insurers play in hospital finance today. On a nationwide basis (Fig. 53) Blue Cross hospital patients occupy higher-cost hospital accommodations than do patients with private insurance policies. Forty-three per cent of the Blue Cross hospital patients admitted occupy rooms with daily rates of $12 or more, and only 25 per cent of

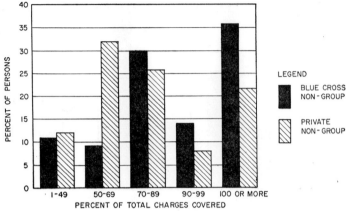

Fig. 52. Percentage distribution of admissions by percentage of hospital bill covered by insurance where some hospital insurance benefits were received, by type of insurance carrier and nongroup enrollment (see Table A-102).

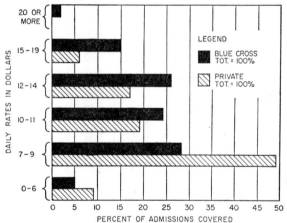

Fig. 53. Percentage distribution of daily room-and-board rates of admission charges, by type of insurance (see Table A-105).

the private-insurance hospital patients admitted occupy such accommodations. Thus the average hospital bill incurred by Blue Cross patients is higher than for private-insurance patients.

Comparisons of benefits from group hospital insurance and individual or nongroup insurance, regardless of type of insurer, reveal that group insurance pays a larger proportion of the hospital charges than nongroup. It is noted (Fig. 54) that 48 per cent of the patients

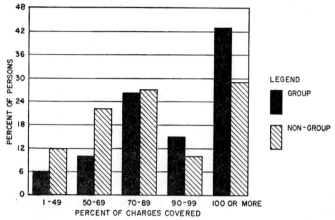

Fig. 54. Percentage distribution of admissions by percentage of hospital bill covered by insurance where some hospital insurance benefits were received, by type of enrollment (see Table A-103).

admitted under group insurance had 90 per cent or more of their hospital charges paid, contrasted with 39 per cent under nongroup insurance.

CHARGES FOR SURGERY

Among people who carried insurance and incurred surgical charges the approximate average charges per individual were $96. This was not strictly charges per case, since a few individuals during the year incurred charges for surgery more than once.

In Table 21 it is noted that surgical patients enrolled in private nongroup surgical insurance incurred charges greater than patients enrolled in other types of insurance.

Table 21. Individuals Covered by One Surgical Policy at the Time of Surgery

Type of insurer	Charges incurred
Blue Shield.....................	$ 94
Private, group..................	95
Private, nongroup...............	107
Independent....................	90

The proportion of incurred surgical charges covered by the various types of insurers is indicated in Table 22. In general, surgical insurance pays for approximately 76 per cent of incurred charges, vary-

Table 22. Individuals Receiving Benefits from Only One Type of Insurer

Type of insurer	Mean per cent covered by insurance	Per cent of individuals with 80% or more covered by insurance
Blue Shield............	78	54
Private, group..........	72	43
Private, nongroup......	66	38
Independent............	94	85

ing from 66 per cent for private nongroup to 94 per cent for the independent plans. The same order holds, although relative differences may be greater, when data are presented showing percentages of individuals incurring surgical charges where 80 per cent or more of such charges was covered by insurance. It should be borne in mind again, as with comparisons of hospital benefits provided by various types of insurers, that no attempt was made to compare premiums in relation to benefits.

CHAPTER *10* *Implications*

What are the implications of the findings in the foregoing chapters for individual and family problems of the costs of personal health services and the present and future status of voluntary health insurance as we know it? Implications cannot be discussed either intelligently or meaningfully without reference to goals and objectives. It would seem that if the goals and objectives are clear there are sufficient data today to point the way to their ultimate attainment.

Thus, a discussion of implications becomes difficult because one has to ask, "Implications in terms of what, and whose goals and objectives?" And, as one reviews the field, it is clear that there is no minimum and tangible standard of achievement agreed to by policy makers in medicine, government, insurance, business, labor, and the rest of the American public even after 20 years of rather intense health-insurance activity and development. This situation is due in part to the unique regard in which personal health services are held. To aspire to a goal of less than 100 per cent of a nebulous concept of perfection is to do violence to the idealism in which personal health services are clothed—*adequate* services, *maximum* quality, and *equal* accessibility—none of which have had scientific yardsticks applied to them yet.

It is then necessary to outline the chief problems and issues in the costs of personal health services and voluntary health insurance today to determine to what degree and where the data in the foregoing chapters assist in the clarification of these problems and issues, perhaps demolishing some, modifying others, and certainly creating new ones.

There would seem to be general agreement that there are two broad problems facing voluntary health insurance today: (1) expansion in terms of people covered, and (2) expansion in terms of benefits offered on an insured or prepaid basis. The first leads to no particular controversy, but the second leads to basic problems of administration, organization of services, concepts of insurability and uninsurability, and many others. These two broad problems are intertwined but can be discussed separately.

ENROLLMENT

Today approximately 100 million people, or 61 per cent of the population, carry some form of health insurance. In all likelihood, approximately 15 per cent of the population cannot or need not be covered by some type of insurance because they are recipients of public assistance, in the armed services, and in institutions. This does not include the undetermined number of people who would not buy health insurance as a matter of choice and inertia. Thus, approximately 72 per cent of the population that can potentially be covered now carries some type of health insurance.

This achievement, phenomenal as it is, cannot be regarded as a valid measure of achievement, since adequate benefits—even when adequacy is defined as 80 per cent of the hospital and surgical costs— is by no means spread evenly over the 100 million or so covered at the present time.

Let us assume that the remaining 28 per cent of the potential population is to be covered by the usual range of benefits now generally available, namely, hospital care and in-hospital physicians' services. It would appear to be undeniable that this 28 per cent—roughly 40 million people—constitutes a segment of the population that is relatively difficult to reach. This segment is characterized by either low income or self-employment and frequently by both. For the low-income group some kind of subsidy from one source or another is certainly indicated. Furthermore, the problem is complicated by a proportion of the population 65 years of age and over not eligible for health insurance because of current underwriting regulations.

In this survey it was revealed that over 70 per cent of the families with incomes over $3,000 were covered by some type of health insurance, and under $3,000 approximately 40 per cent of the families were covered. The elimination of the 5 to 6 million recipients of public assistance increases the latter percentage only slightly. It is likely that further coverage of incomes over $3,000 represents an enrollment problem of individuals and small groups, and among low-income groups there are problems of both low income and lack of a common employer. Enrollment, so far, has been predominantly through group enrollment with payroll deductions. Methods need to be found to enroll individuals and small groups at a reasonable administrative cost and with benefits at least comparable to those received by persons enrolled in groups. Previous evidence has shown that benefits under individual contracts are not so broad as those under group contracts.

NATIONWIDE CHARGES FOR PERSONAL HEALTH SERVICES

In absolute terms $10.2 billion for private personal health services for the nation would seem to be a very large sum of money. In perspective, however, this sum is only 4 to 5 per cent of the national personal income and would seem to be a relatively small amount to pay for an extremely important part of our national and individual well-being. Thus, the absolute amount paid out for personal health services is not regarded as too high—it might well be higher—but the problem is one of spreading this cost over all families through insurance premiums. This is certainly no new idea, but it bears repetition time and again.

The national sum of $10.2 billion is translated into $207 per family, ranging from $130 for families with incomes under $2,000 to $353 for families with incomes over $7,500. In all likelihood, some families below $2,000 received free services or services at a reduced cost, but a higher percentage of their incomes was laid out for care than among families with incomes over $7,500, medians of 6.2 per cent and 3.3 per cent respectively. Thus, low-income families paid for a larger share of the costs in terms of their incomes than higher-income groups. It would seem to be a generally accepted principle that costs should be spread in accordance with ability to pay, and it is obvious that they are not so spread today. Increasing insurance, in terms of both people and benefits, will tend to spread costs according to income.

Families with insurance incurred appreciably higher charges for all types of services than families without insurance. The mean gross charges for families with insurance were $237 and for families without insurance, $154. The medians were $145 and $63 respectively. An increase in utilization, in turn, reflected in higher gross charges, would be expected, but it is interesting to note that insured families incurred appreciably higher charges for uninsured services as well, such as dentistry and drugs and medications outside the hospital. Whether or not this was due to the presence or absence of insurance cannot be stated categorically, at this time, but it is clear that the whole level of utilization and charges was higher among insured families than uninsured families. This was true for all income levels. In fact, it is evident that the lower the income the greater was the impact of insurance in increasing cost and utilization relative to the uninsured families in the same income group. Since 77 per cent of the families who were insured obtained their insurance through their place of employment in a group, it would seem that the factor of self-selection of high health risks would be minimized but certainly not eliminated. Thus, the relatively high utilization and costs among insured families compared with uninsured families cannot be readily explained.

If the entire population were covered by the currently prevailing types of insurance benefits, the total costs of all private personal health services would in theory rise from $10.2 billion to approximately $11.7, or an increase of $1.5 billion, exclusive of costs of administration. Speculating further, if all persons were covered by the prevailing types of hospital-insurance benefits, the total hospital charges for private patients might rise from $2.0 billion to approximately $2.5, or an increase of $500 million. It should be emphasized, however, that this is speculation.

DISTRIBUTION OF CHARGES AMONG FAMILIES AND INDIVIDUALS

The fact that costs of personal health services fall unevenly on families and individuals in the course of a year was a corroboration of one of the basic findings of the Committee on the Costs of Medical Care 25 years ago. Because of this characteristic it has been possible to devise insurance plans enabling groups of people to budget a small amount of money periodically to be used as needed when charges for personal health services are incurred.

The principle of insurance to help meet costs of personal health services is accepted, but there is debate regarding the range of benefits which should and can be offered in a health-insurance program. Many assert that the home and office calls and so-called "minor" cost items should not be covered by insurance because they represent small and periodic charges which can be borne out of pocket. If we approach personal health service primarily from the financial side, how unevenly do costs fall by type of service? Using the figure of approximately $200 as a relatively high charge to incur during a year, 34 per cent of all families incur charges of this magnitude for all services. Classified by type of service, 3 per cent of the families incur charges in excess of approximately $200 for surgery; 6 per cent, for physicians' services other than surgery and obstetrics; 6 per cent, for hospital services; 2 per cent, for medicines; and 4 per cent, for dentistry. It is apparent that over a year more families incur charges in excess of $200 for physicians' services other than surgery and obstetrics than for surgery. It would seem that the economic impact of services other than surgery and hospital care is also important and cannot be ignored in a health-insurance program, particularly for illnesses that are relatively costly. It should also be borne in mind that the above costs frequently overlap for families, i.e., families who incur charges of $200 for hospital care also incur charges for other services simultaneously.

During the past few years a new type of health-insurance contract called "major medical" has been promoted by an increasing number of health-insurance plans and companies. Some of the proponents of this type of contract feel that the family could well afford to pay the first $100 to $500 charges for personal health services directly or with the help of a limited type of contract, after which health insurance pays the major portion, such as 75 per cent. From the data in this survey, 46 per cent of the families incur no charges or charges of less than $100 or so; 66 per cent incur charges of less than $200, and 89 per cent incur charges under $500. If a major-medical contract covered charges in excess of $100 with no co-insurance, it would cover 64 per cent of all charges, assuming such charges were paid in full. If the lower limit were $200 with no co-insurance, a major-medical contract would pay 46 per cent of such charges. Jumping to a higher limit of $500 and no co-insurance, a major-medical contract would be paying 18 per cent of all charges in excess of this figure. If a 25 per cent co-insurance factor were added, major-medical contracts covering charges in excess of $100 would be paying approximately 48 per cent of all charges. If the limit were $200, a major-medical contract with 25 per cent co-insurance would pay 34 per cent of all charges. If the limit were $500, a major-medical contract with 25 per cent co-insurance would then be paying 13 per cent of total charges. Admittedly, all this is speculative, but it is based on valid information. It should help in the comprehension of the massive problems with which we are dealing.

HEALTH INSURANCE AND THE CHARGES
FOR PERSONAL HEALTH SERVICES

One of the chief reasons for the present survey was to determine the influence of insurance on current costs and utilization of personal health services and the cushioning of that cost. Again, there is no general agreement on what is "adequate" cushioning of cost, but it is hoped that the foregoing data have assisted in arriving at some concept of "adequacy."

If we limit our concept of adequacy to hospitalization, surgery, and obstetrics, which together make up 31 per cent of the medical dollar, prevailing health-insurance benefits cover approximately 50 per cent of all private-patient hospital charges, 38 per cent of all surgical charges, and 25 per cent of all obstetrical charges for the entire population. Accordingly, assuming 90 per cent payment for these services to allow for deductibles and so on, insurance has 40 per cent of the hospital charges left to cover the entire population, 52 per cent of the surgical charges, and 65 per cent of the charges for obstetrics. If it is assumed that *all* physicians' services should be covered by insurance, allowing for a deductible of 10 per cent, 77 per cent of such charges remain to be covered. Other services are an open question, as yet, except possibly in major-medical contracts.

Among the insured segment of the population, if it is desired to upgrade hospital insurance so that all families with insurance and receiving hospital care have at least 80 per cent of their hospital charges paid by insurance, it is evident that approximately 41 per cent of the families so situated need a better type of hospital-insurance contract. Similarly, if it is desired to upgrade surgical insurance so that all families with insurance and receiving surgical service have at least 80 per cent of surgical charges covered by insurance, approximately 55 per cent of the families now covered need a better type of surgical-insurance contract. For obstetrical services of physicians, excluding hospital care, 65 per cent of the families now insured need a better type of contract covering obstetrical services in order to have at least 80 per cent of charges for such services covered. The above would appear to be minimum goals to which almost everyone concerned would agree.

UTILIZATION OF HOSPITAL CARE AND SURGERY

The evidence is strongly suggestive that insurance influences the utilization of hospital care in that insured persons have an admission rate of 14 per 100 and uninsured persons a rate of 9. These rates are a matter of fact and undeniable, but the degree of self-selection among the insured is not known. It is true that 77 per cent of those with insurance were enrolled through groups, and they therefore obtained their insurance more or less through chance. Nevertheless, there may be self-selection among them in that persons who accepted insurance in an employed group, and persons who obtained insurance as individuals, were more desirous of health services than those without insurance. A greater knowledge of attitudes and practices is also necessary, as well as knowledge of insurance coverage, in order to explain fully the higher admission rates of insured persons compared with those uninsured.

Insured individuals in low-income groups have a higher hospital-admission rate than insured individuals in higher-income groups. Again, the degree of self-selection is not known. The same is true for insured rural farm persons compared with insured persons in urban areas. Lacking definitive information, one can speculate endlessly on the reasons for these differences which may vary from a backlog of unmet need to so-called "abuse" or overuse.

It is easy to write a long essay on the concept of abuse or overuse, and such an essay is not intended here, but in the face of mounting utilization and concurrent costs during the past 20 years it is tempting to attribute them to abuse and overuse. It should be recalled, however, that there exist no definite criteria of when a person should or should not be hospitalized. Hospital care is as much a function of a going standard of living as it is of medical judgment. Criteria for hospital admissions emerge from the patterns of practice of many physicians in the community and from the desires and needs of their patients. Certainly the concept of abuse or overuse needs a thorough analysis in several hospitals before quick allegations are made.

In our concern with the aged, hospital care becomes a major problem relative to the rest of the population. Persons 65 years of age and over are hospitalized more often than any other age group (except females 18 to 34), and they stay in the hospital longer. At the same time it is difficult for them to obtain insurance because of their age.

The utilization of surgical services shows the same patterns as those of hospital services. Persons with surgical insurance experience more surgery than persons without insurance, and insured persons in rural farm areas experience more surgery than insured persons in urban areas. Also, insured persons in low-income groups experience more surgery than insured persons in higher-income groups.

Again, to what extent does the presence or absence of insurance influence the surgical rate, and to what extent are there factors of self-selection involved? It would seem that need for surgery could be established more easily than need for hospitalization of nonsurgical patients, thus making it difficult to explain the great difference in surgical rates among insured and uninsured. Insured persons experience a surgical rate of 9 per 100, and uninsured persons a rate of 5. By any stretch of the imagination, however, it would seem unreasonable to assume that insured persons experience 4 "unnecessary" surgical procedures per 100. There are a great many unknown factors involved which warrant a thorough analysis.

TYPES OF INSURERS IN RELATION TO BENEFITS AND UTILIZATION OF SERVICES

Since this study is primarily an economic study of the distribution of the costs of personal health services and the effect of voluntary health insurance in spreading the costs of such services, there is no concern here with an analysis of the different types of arrangements for providing or paying for services such as Blue Cross and Blue Shield, private insurance companies, and group-practice salaried types of insurance plans. The only point of comparison between the different types of organizations is the extent to which they spread the costs of personal health services. If the objective is to cover almost 100 per cent of the costs of all personal health services, obviously the insurance plans which offer or pay for the widest range of services are the most desirable. If the objective is to cushion high-cost services and illnesses, leaving to the individual family the responsibility of paying for all other services directly, then another set of criteria must be used.

In one type of arrangement, the present structure of hospital and physicians' services is left intact. The chief change has been in the source of payment. In the other type of arrangement there usually is a basic reorganization of physicians' services, notably in the manner of payment of physicians, namely, salary or some type of capitation. Further, in the former type of arrangement there is usually no attempt to provide whatever is defined as organized preventive services, whereas in the group-practice type of arrangement there is such an attempt. This is not to imply, however, that preventive services are not sought and provided in the prevailing pattern of practice.

The great proportion of the health insurance in this country is written by Blue Cross and Blue Shield and by private insurance companies. Group-practice insurance plans cover a small proportion of the population, although they are growing gradually. Thus, on a national level the chief competition in insurance is between Blue Cross and Blue Shield on the one hand and private insurance on the other. It is apparent that in group insurance Blue Cross–Blue Shield and private insurance cover approximately the same proportions of the hospital and surgical charges. This comparison is made with no reference to premium charges. To the extent that Blue Cross and Blue Shield have attempted individual enrollment, however, their benefits are greater than those of their counterparts in private insurance.

There are many other factors which must be taken into account in order to evaluate the respective merits of the different types of insurance plans. Although they were not a part of this study, it is well to mention them. They are (1) type of sponsorship, (2) locus of control of policy, (3) premium charges, (4) range of benefits, and (5) service type of benefit vs. indemnity type of benefit. Perhaps in the future it will be possible to devise a composite index of quality of a particular type of insurance plan which will combine the economic factors, with which this study has been primarily concerned, with factors listed above. Before this can be done meaningfully, however, a clearer concept must prevail of what are desirable and adequate goals and objectives. Desirable as this may be, it is likely that developments in health insurance, as in almost any other line of human endeavor, are not necessarily the outcome of well-reasoned choices from many possible alternatives. Rather, the form that health insurance has taken and will take is a tenuous balance between the many elements that make up the complexities of personal health services: people, hospitals, physicians, insurance, and finance, interlaced with philosophies of government and private enterprise and with the level of public information and knowledge.

APPENDIX A

Statistical Tables

Table A-1. Estimated Number of Persons Having Voluntary Health Insurance, by Kind of Insurer, July, 1953

Type of protection and kind of insurer*	Persons in sample with coverage, %	Estimated number in civilian non-institutional population,† millions
Total, with some protection...................	58	90.2
Hospital, net total, after eliminating duplication	*57*	*88.1‡*
Blue Cross..............................	27	41.2
Private insurance, group...................	17	26.7
Private insurance, nongroup...............	12	18.4
Independent and other....................	6	9.8
Surgical or medical, net total, after eliminating duplication.....................	*49*	*75.2§*
Blue Shield and Blue Cross................	19	29.6
Private insurance, group...................	17	26.3
Private insurance, nongroup...............	10	15.2
Independent and other....................	7	10.4
Other:		
Poliomyelitis and "dread disease"..........	4	6.6
Major medical expense...................	¶	0.3

* In classifying insurers, the definitions were those used in *Building America's Health: Financing a Health Program for America*, A Report to the President, The President's Commisson on the Health Needs of the Nation, 1953, Vol. 4. See Table 11.5, especially footnotes to p. 336.

† The civilian noninstitutional population for July, 1953, is estimated at 154.6 million. Based on U.S. Bureau of the Census, *Current Population Reports. Population Estimates*, ser. P-25, no. 79, and *U.S. Census of Population: 1950*, vol. IV, Special Reports, pt. 2, chap. C, "Institutional Population," p. 13.

‡ Since a good many individuals (about eight million) were covered by more than one kind of insurer for hospital expenses, this net total is less than the sum of the totals for the different kinds of insurers. The net total of 88.1 million represents the number of persons with hospital-expense protection, eliminating duplication by two or more *different kinds* of insurers. Another 1.6 million persons had two or more plans or policies with the *same kind of insurer* covering hospital expenses, but this kind of duplication does not appear in the totals for the different kinds of insurers which show *number of persons* covered by *one or more* group private, nongroup private, etc., hospital policies. After eliminating for duplication, it is estimated that 43.4 million individuals were covered by group and/or nongroup private hospital insurance.

§ These figures include 4.5 million persons who belong to plans which provide substantially complete medical service; the remainder are covered only for surgical fees or for limited medical service.

This net total of 75.2 million represents the number of persons with surgical or medical-expense protection, after eliminating duplication of such coverage by two or more *different kinds* of insurers for 6.3 million persons. Another 1.8 million persons have two or more plans or policies with the *same kind* of insurer, but this kind of duplication does not appear in the totals for the different kinds of insurers. After eliminating for duplication, it is estimated that 40.2 million individuals were covered by group and/or nongroup private surgical insurance.

¶ Less than half of 1%.

Table A-2. Percentage of Persons in Each Geographical Region with Voluntary Health Insurance, by Type of Coverage

Region	Per cent of persons, by type of coverage	
	Hospital*	Surgical or medical†
Total..................	57	48
Northeast..............	62	48
North Central..........	64	56
South.................	50	44
West..................	47	43

* These figures are net of estimated duplication, i.e., they represent the percentage of persons covered by at least one hospital plan or policy.

† These figures are net of estimated duplication, i.e., they represent the percentage of persons covered by at least one surgical or medical insurance plan or policy.

Table *A-3*. Percentage of Those Covered by Hospital Insurance Who Were
Covered under Contracts of Specified Types, by Regional Location*

Type of contract †	Per cent covered, by region				
	All regions	Northeast	North Central	South	West
All persons covered (group and non-group)..........	57 (5,042 = 100%)	62 (1,371 = 100%)	64 (1,671 = 100%)	50 (1,418 = 100%)	47 (582 = 100%)
Group..............	*73*	*78*	*73*	*67*	*77*
Blue Cross........	36	50	44	23	16
Private...........	30	22	30	37	34
Independent.......	10	10	2	10	33
Nongroup...........	*32*	*27*	*32*	*38*	*28*
Blue Cross........	10	16	10	6	8
Private...........	21	10	21	33	18
Independent.......	1	1	2	1	2

* Only people covered by hospital insurance at the end of the survey year are included.

† Seven contracts of unknown type were excluded from the numerators of these percentages, but included in the denominators.

Since some individuals had contracts of two or more different types, the sum of the percentages having each type equals more than 100%. Since some individuals had more than one group contract, the sum of the percentages having each of the different types of group contracts is greater than the percentage having one or more group contracts. The same is true of individual or nongroup contracts.

Table A-4. Percentage of Families with Voluntary Health Insurance,
by Income Group

Annual family income*	Number of families	Families with some coverage, %
Total, all families.........	2,809	63
Under $3,000............	976	41
$3,000–$4,999...........	912	71
5,000 and over..........	903	80
Income unknown.........	18	†

* This breakdown by family income shows roughly the lowest third with family income under $3,000, the middle third with family income $3,000 to $4,999, and the highest third with family income $5,000 and over.

† Percentages not computed for groups of less than 50 families.

Table A-5. Percentage Distribution of Persons Covered by Hospital Insurance, by Type of Enrollment and Income*

Family income	Number of persons with hospital insurance‡	Per cent covered, by type of enrollment†	
		Group	Nongroup
Total, all individuals...........	5,042	73	32
Under $2,000..................	356	41	62
$2,000–$3,499................	925	67	37
3,500– 4,999................	1,524	79	25
5,000– 7,499................	1,392	79	25
7,500 and over...............	832	73	36

* Only people covered by hospital insurance at the end of the survey year are included.

† Since some individuals are enrolled in both group and nongroup, the sum of the percentages having each type equals more than 100%.

‡ Figures equal 100%.

Table A-6. Percentage Distribution of Persons Covered by Hospital Insurance, by Type of Insurer and Type of Contract, by Income*

Type of contract†	Per cent covered, by family income					
	All income groups	$0–$1,999	$2,000–$3,499	$3,500–$4,999	$5,000–$7,499	$7,500 and over
All persons covered (group and nongroup)........	57	26	48	64	71	71
	(5,042 = 100%)	(356 = 100%)	(925 = 100%)	(1,524 = 100%)	(1,392 = 100%)	(832 = 100%)
Group.................	*73*	*41*	*67*	*79*	*79*	*73*
Blue cross.............	36	10	30	43	39	39
Private..............	30	17	34	29	33	29
Independent.........	10	14	4	9	13	8
Nongroup..............	*32*	*62*	*37*	*25*	*25*	*36*
Blue Cross...........	10	6	11	8	10	16
Private..............	21	54	25	16	15	19
Independent.........	1	3	1	1	1	1

* Only people covered by hospital insurance at the end of the survey year are included.
† Since some individuals had contracts with two or more types of insurers, the sum of the percentages having each type equals more than 100%.

Table A-7. Percentage Distribution of Persons Covered by Hospital Insurance, by Type of Insurer and Type of Contract, by Residence*

Type of contract† and insurer	Per cent covered, by residence				
	All areas	Urban, areas of 1 million or more	Other urban	Rural nonfarm	Rural farm
All persons covered (group and non-group)............	57	63	65	52	38
	(5,042 = 100%)	(1,446 = 100%)	(2,033 = 100%)	(944 = 100%)	(619 = 100%)
Group..............	*73*	*80*	*73*	*75*	*52*
Blue Cross........	36	53	34	26	21
Private..........	30	26	34	36	21
Independent.......	10	6	9	17	12
Nongroup..........	*32*	*25*	*31*	*30*	*53*
Blue Cross........	10	12	9	10	11
Private..........	21	11	22	20	41
Independent.......	1	1	1	1	2

* Only people covered by hospital insurance at the end of the survey year are included.

Since some individuals had contracts with two or more types of insurers, the sum of the percentage having each type equals more than 100%.

† Seven contracts of unknown type were excluded from the numerators of these percentages but included in the denominators.

Table A-8. Percentage Distribution of Persons Covered by Hospital Insurance,
by Type of Enrollment and Residence*

Residence	Number of persons with hospital insurance‡	Per cent covered, by type of enrollment†	
		Group	Nongroup
All areas.....................	5,042	73	32
Urban, areas of 1 million or more	1,446	80	25
Other urban..................	2,033	73	31
Rural nonfarm...............	944	75	30
Rural farm..................	619	52	53

* Only people covered by hospital insurance at the end of the survey year are included.

† Since some individuals are enrolled in both group and nongroup, the sum of the percentages having each type equals more than 100%.

‡ Figures equal 100%.

Table A-9. Percentage of Families with Voluntary Health Insurance,
by Industry of Main Earner

Industry of family's main earner	Number of families	Families with some coverage, %
Total, main earner currently working full time........	2,429	69
Agriculture, forestry, and fisheries.................	302	33
Mining...	75	89
Construction.......................................	181	57
Manufacturing....................................	705*	87*
Durable goods...............................	*376*	*85*
Nondurable goods............................	*316*	*90*
Transportation, communication, and public utilities ..	203	74
Wholesale and retail trade........................	375	67
Finance, insurance, real estate, and business services..	80	71
Personal services and repair services...............	144	49
Entertainment and recreation services..............	28	†
Professional and related services...................	137	72
Public administration and armed forces‡............	140	65
Industry indeterminate...........................	59	71

* This figure contains 13 families where it was impossible to determine whether the main earner worked in a durable or nondurable goods industry.

† Percentages not computed for groups of fewer than 50 families.

‡ 30% of the families with main earner in the armed forces but living off-post with his family had some coverage.

Table A-10. Percentage of Families with Voluntary Health Insurance,
by Educational Attainment of Main Earner

Years of schooling completed by main earner in family	Number of families	Per cent of total families	Families with some coverage, %
Total, all families....................	2,809	100	63
No schooling.......................	57	2.0	35
Elementary:			
1 to 4 years.....................	219	7.8	39
5 to 6 years.....................	223	7.9	52
7 to 8 years.....................	679	24.2	61
High school:			
1 to 3 years.....................	578	20.6	66
4 years.........................	551	19.6	73
College:			
1 to 3 years.....................	253	9.0	74
4 years.........................	207	7.3	76
School years not reported............	42	1.5	40
Median years of school completed by main earner = 10.1*............			

* Median years of school completed by main earner in families with some
coverage is 10.9 and in families with no coverage, 9.7.

Table A-11. Percentage of Persons with Hospital Insurance, by Age and Sex

Age and sex	Number of persons	Persons with hospital insurance, %
All persons (males and females), total	*8,846*	*57*
Under 6.............................	1,171	57
6–17................................	1,851	58
18–24...............................	699	49
25–34...............................	1,258	64
35–44...............................	1,330	65
45–54...............................	997	63
55–64...............................	773	54
65 and over.........................	740	31
Age unknown........................	27	*
Males, total............................	*4,284*	*57*
Under 6.............................	584	55
6–17................................	936	58
18–24...............................	308	42
25–34...............................	599	63
35–44...............................	637	64
45–54...............................	496	65
55–64...............................	363	56
65 and over.........................	351	35
Age unknown........................	10	*
Females, total..........................	*4,562*	*57*
Under 6.............................	587	59
6–17................................	915	59
18–24...............................	391	67
25–34...............................	659	65
35–44...............................	693	65
45–54...............................	501	61
55–64...............................	410	52
65 and over.........................	389	26
Age unknown........................	17	*

* Percentages not computed for groups of fewer than 50 individuals.

Table A-12. Percentage of Families with Voluntary Health Insurance,
by Sex and Age of Family Head

Age and sex of family head	Number of families	Families with some coverage, %
Total, all families.............	2,809	63
With male head, total..........	*2,406*	*66*
Under 25.................	104	62
25–29....................	222	72
30–34....................	303	69
35–44....................	613	72
45–54....................	476	70
55–64....................	352	66
65–74....................	239	50
75 and over...............	79	35
Age indeterminate..........	18	39
With female head, total..........	*403*	*48*
Under 35.................	52	56
35–44....................	53	53
45–54....................	65	69
55–64....................	89	55
65–74....................	84	32
75 and over...............	55	27
Age indeterminate..........	5	40

Table A-13. Estimated National Total Gross Charges Incurred by Families for All Personal Health Services and Goods

Service or goods	NORC sample July, 1952, through June, 1953		Department of Commerce estimates for 1952	
	Amount, billions	Per cent	Amount, billions	Per cent
Total............................	$10.2	100	$8.8	100
Physicians........................	3.8	37	2.8	32
Hospitals.........................	2.0	20	2.4	27
Prescriptions and other medicines	1.5	15	1.6	18
Other medical goods and services.....	1.3	13	1.0	11
Dentists..........................	1.6	16	1.0	11

SOURCE: U.S. Department of Commerce, *Survey of Current Business, National Income Number*, July, 1953, Table 30, p. 22. Since the Department of Commerce estimate has recently been showing about a 6% increase in expenditures per year, it seems likely that Department of Commerce figures for the survey period would be about 3% higher than those presented here.

Physicians' costs can be further broken down into (1) surgery: 0.8 billion, 21%; (2) obstetrics: 0.4 billion, 11%; (3) other physicians: 2.6 billions, 68%.

The NORC estimate of total payments to physicians is not exactly comparable to the Department of Commerce estimate for a number of reasons. The following indicates how various marginal items are handled in the two estimates: (1) Payments to hospital outpatient departments for the services of salaried physicians and other clinical services are classified under *Physicians* by NORC and *Hospitals* by Department of Commerce. (2) Payments by either consumers or insurance for medical services received from salaried physicians in government hospitals are classified under *Physicians* by NORC and are excluded by Department of Commerce. (3) Value of services of salaried physician in a government or private hospital or clinic or the services of a company doctor when such services were not paid for by the patient and were not received as part of any form of prepaid medical-care plan or insurance is excluded in both. (4) Estimated value (at going rates) of physicians' services received from salaried physicians under some form of prepaid medical-care plan are classified under *Physicians* by NORC and are excluded by Department of Commerce. (5) Free care (care for which an independent physician received no reimbursement and did not bill anyone) is excluded by both. (6) Payments to independent physicians (physicians in private practice) by workmen's compensation, employer's liability insurance, or by an employer for a work-incurred injury are excluded by both. (7) Vendor payments to independent physicians under governmental (generally state or local) assistance programs for various categories of indigent families are excluded by both. (8) Vendor payments to independent physicians by foundations and associations like the National Tuberculosis Institute, National Foundation for Infantile Paralysis, Crippled Children's Societies, Rotary, Lions, etc., are excluded by NORC and probably generally excluded by Department of Commerce. (9) Payments to independent

Table A-13 (Continued)

physicians by recipients under governmental assistance programs when these payments were specifically reimbursed to the recipient by the program are generally excluded by NORC and probably generally included under *Physicians* by Department of Commerce. (10) Payments by surgical or medical insurance to independent physicians, either directly or through reimbursement of the patient, are under *Physicians* in both. (11) Payments by accident insurance or liability insurance (except employer's liability insurance or workmen's compensation) to independent physicians, either directly or through reimbursement of patient, are under *Physicians* in both. (12) Payments for drugs administered by a physician is under *Physicians* in both. (13) Payments to independent physicians for medical care received by people who were not part of the civilian, noninstitutional population of the continental United States as of July, 1953, is excluded by NORC (except as indicated in 14 and 15, and is classified under *Physicians* by Department of Commerce. (14) Payments to independent physicians for services received by persons who were still considered as members of some household in July, 1953, even though they had been institutionalized at some time during the past year and were still in an institution on the date of interview, are under *Physicians* in both. (15) Payments to independent physicians for services received by people who died during the survey year but who had been living at the time of their death with relatives as members of households still in existence in July, 1953, are under *Physicians* in both. (This category thus excludes deceased who had been living in institutions, alone, or only with nonrelatives at the time of their death as well as those who lived in households which were broken up after the death.) (16) Bad debts (services by physicians for which patients were actually billed but which will never be paid for) are classified under *Physicians* by NORC and are excluded by Department of Commerce.

It is also possible that physicians may sometimes act as collecting agents for the fees for certain clinical services like X-rays, laboratory work, or special tests which they themselves do not perform. The physician may net no income from this and so does not consider these fees as part of his gross income. NORC in general classified all such fees paid to a physician into the *Physician* category, while the Department of Commerce may conceivably have excluded such payments. It should be noted that the NORC estimate is derived from a distinctively different type of survey from that of the Department of Commerce. The NORC estimate is derived from the expenditures reported by consumers who were still part of the civilian, noninstitutional population of continental United States at the end of the survey year. The Department of Commerce estimate is based on voluntary reports of gross income by physicians in private practice in response to a mail questionnaire survey conducted by the Department of Commerce. The responses to either or both surveys may have been subject to an overreporting or underreporting bias of a fairly substantial nature, but since these two types of surveys are certainly the two most reliable known ways of making such an estimate, it is certainly a matter of conjecture as to which estimate is more nearly correct. A further examination of the two estimates is contemplated for the future. The main difference between the NORC and the Department of Commerce estimate of total expenditures for hospital care is that NORC has practically excluded payments for care in long-term hospitals (because many of the patients in long-term hospitals are not considered as part of any noninstitutional household and thus do not have expenditures reported for them), while the Department of Commerce does include the costs of such care. Actually, this difference in approach

Table A-13 (Continued)

has little practical consequence, because the Department of Commerce estimate is concerned exclusively with nongovernmental hospitals, while an overwhelming proportion of long-term hospital facilities are in fact governmental. Another difference of some importance is in the treatment of expenditures for outpatient care in hospitals. NORC has classified expenditures for emergency care under *Hospitals;* for physician's care, under *Physicians;* and for laboratory, X-rays, and similar diagnostic services, under *Other.* The Department of Commerce has classified all such outpatient expenditures under *Hospitals.* A third difference is in connection with the treatment of free or reduced-rate care in nongovernmental nonprofit hospitals. NORC has excluded the value of such care when it was not connected with any form of prepaid medical-care plan or insurance. Since the Department of Commerce estimate is based on the expenditures rather than the patient income of these nonprofit hospitals, the costs of free and reduced-rate care are included in their estimate. Both estimates for *Prescriptions and Other Medicines* are for pharmaceuticals purchased directly by the consumer. The expenditures for pharmaceuticals administered in hospitals or by physicians and dentists are included in the estimated payments to those groups and are excluded from this item. The NORC estimate on *Other Medical Goods and Services* contains expenditures for medical appliances including ophthalmic products; services of oculists and optometrists; services of paramedical personnel like chiropractors, chiropodists, podiatrists, naturopaths, faith healers, etc.; the services of private-duty nurses, practical nurses, and midwives; and expenditures for laboratory services like diagnostic tests and X-rays for which the consumer was billed directly by the laboratory. The Department of Commerce estimate contains essentially the same items except for the expenditures for laboratory and X-ray services. It is not clear where the Department of Commerce includes these latter categories of expense. (Osteopathic physicians are included in *Physicians* in both NORC and Department of Commerce figures.) The Department of Commerce estimate on *Dentists* is based on voluntary reports of gross income by dentists in private practice in response to a mail questionnaire survey conducted by the Department of Commerce. The NORC estimate is based on expenditure reports by consumers. It should be noted that the NORC estimate contains expenditures made directly to dental laboratories for X-rays, denture repair, and the manufacture of dentures on the basis of impressions taken by dentists. These expenditures may have been excluded from the Department of Commerce estimate.

Table A-14. Estimated National Percentages of Total Gross Charges Incurred by Families Covered by Total Insurance Benefits, by Type of Service (July, 1952, through June, 1953)

Service or goods	Total gross costs incurred, billions	Total insurance benefits, billions	Per cent covered by insurance benefits
Total..................	$10.2	$1.5	15
Hospitals*..............	2.0	1.0	50
Physicians.............	3.8	0.5	13
Surgery..............	*0.8*	*0.3*	*38*
Obstetrics............	*0.4*	*0.1*	*25*
Other physicians......	*2.6*	*0.1*	*4*
Medicines..............	1.5	†	0
Other medical goods and services..............	1.3	†	1
Dentists..............	1.6	†	0

* Since many patients in nongovernmental general and special long-term hospitals, mental and allied hospitals, and tuberculosis sanatoria at the time of the interviewing may not have been considered as members of civilian noninstitutional households, the NORC estimate probably does not adequately represent expenditures for this category of care.

† Less than $50 million.

Table A-15. Mean and Median Gross Charges Incurred by Families for
All Personal Health Services, by Family Income and Insurance Status

Family Income	Number of families			Mean gross charges*			Median gross charges*		
	All families	In-sured	Unin-sured	All families	In-sured	Unin-sured	All families	In-sured	Unin-sured
Total, all income groups......	2,809	1,780	1,029	$207	$237	$154	$110	$145	$ 63
Under $2,000...............	576	180	396	130	164	115	54	82	43
$2,000–$3,499...............	613	345	268	152	168	132	82	103	54
3,500– 4,999...............	699	520	179	207	220	167	119	134	83
5,000– 7,499...............	566	458	108	259	262	247	176	187	105
7,500 and over,.............	337	272	65	353	362	312	238	255	185
Income unknown.............	18	5	13						

* Gross charges are all charges incurred by the family unit for its own members for hospital, medical, and dental services and goods. They do not include costs of voluntary health insurance. The "cost" of free care is, of course, excluded. However, the cost of services received under a hospital service plan or a comprehensive medical-care plan is included.

Table A-16. Aggregate Family Total Outlay for Medical Care as a Percentage
of Aggregate Family Income, and Medians of the Distributions of
Family Total Outlay as Percentages of Family Income
for Families, by Income and Insurance Status

Family income (all families with known incomes)	Number of families			Aggregate family total outlay,* % of aggregate family income†			Median of family total outlay,* % of aggregate family income‡		
	All families	With insurance	With no insurance	All families	With insurance	With no insurance	All families	With insurance	With no insurance
Total, all income groups	2,791	1,775	1,016	4.8	4.8	4.8	4.1	4.4	3.0
Under $2,000..........	576	180	396	11.8	13.4	11.0	6.2	10.2	4.8
$2,000–$3,499..........	613	345	268	6.1	6.6	5.3	4.0	5.1	2.6
3,500– 4,999..........	699	520	179	5.4	5.8	4.2	3.9	4.4	2.2
5,000– 7,499..........	566	458	108	4.7	4.9	4.2	3.6	3.9	2.2
7,500 and over........	337	272	65	3.0§	3.1§	2.8§	3.3¶	3.3¶	3.0¶

* Family total outlay for medical care was defined as the family's actual cash outlay during the survey year for personal health services and voluntary prepayment for such services. It is made up of the following components: (1) *gross total costs* for personal health services received during survey year, minus (2) *insurance benefits* covering personal health services received during survey year, minus (3) *amounts still owed* for personal health services received during survey year, plus (4) *insurance premiums* for insurance designed to cover the costs of personal health services, plus (5) *payments made by the family for personal health services received by persons who were not family members at the end of the year*, plus (6) *payments made during the survey year on old bills* for personal health services received prior to the survey year. It was occasionally not possible to distinguish that part of a combined premium payment intended for hospital, surgical, and medical care insurance from that part of the combined premium intended for disability, accident, or life insurance. The family total outlay may therefore have been occasionally overstated by an extremely small amount.

† The outlays of all families in a given income–insurance-status group were aggregated and taken as a percentage of the aggregate income for that subgroup.

‡ *The outlay of each family* was taken as a percentage of that family's income. The statistics presented here are the medians of the distributions of those percentages within the particular subgroups. Thus, half the families in the survey laid·out more than 4.1% of their incomes for medical care, while the other half laid out less than that percentage of their incomes.

§ The exact incomes of families who stated their income to be greater than $10,000 was not collected on this survey. An estimate was made of the aggregate income of those families with more than $10,000 income on the basis of Supplementary Table 11 to "1954 Survey of Consumer Finances: The Financial Position and Commitments of Consumers," *Federal Reserve Bulletin*, July, 1954. It was

Table A-16 (Continued)

assumed that the mean income for families with more than $10,000 income was equal for insured and noninsured families. Although there is some reason to believe that the noninsured families in this income group had larger incomes than the insured families, the error introduced through the present method of estimation is probably not appreciable.

¶ Since the exact incomes of families who stated their income to be greater than $10,000 was not available, the income of each family in this group was taken to be $10,000 for this computation. Thus, the medians presented for the $7,500-and-over income group may conceivably be too high by as much as one-half of 1%, although the actual error is probably smaller than that. This income group constitutes such a small proportion of the total population that it is highly unlikely that the medians for "all families with known income" could be affected by more than one-tenth of 1% by the underestimate of income for the $10,000-and-over group.

Table A-17. Mean Gross Charges per Family for Personal Health Services,
by Residence and Type of Service
(Columns do not add up to totals because of rounding)

Type of service	Charges, by residence				
	All areas	Urban, areas of 1 million or more	Other urban	Rural nonfarm	Rural farm
All services............	$207	$237	$204	$197	$178
Physicians............	78	91	74	79	69
Hospitals............	41	39	44	42	35
Medicines............	31	32	29	30	33
Other...............	26	27	27	25	25
Dentists............	33	51	31	24	19

Table A-18. Mean Gross Charges per Family, by Type of Service,
Residence, and Insurance Status
(Columns do not add up to totals because of rounding)

Type of service	Charges, by residence and insurance status											
	Urban, areas of 1 million or more			Other urban			Rural nonfarm			Rural farm		
	All families	In- sured	Unin- sured	All families	In- sured	Unin- sured	All families	In- sured	Unin- sured	All families	In- sured	Unin- sured
All services..........	$237	$270	$149	$204	$232	$144	$197	$212	$177	$178	$213	$150
Physicians...........	91	104	54	74	82	56	79	83	73	69	76	63
Hospitals............	39	44	23	44	53	25	42	44	39	35	52	21
Medicines...........	32	36	22	29	31	24	30	31	30	33	39	28
Other...............	27	30	18	27	29	23	25	27	23	25	26	25
Dentists.............	51	70	32	31	37	20	24	30	16	19	27	13

Table A-19. Mean Gross Charges per Family for All Personal Health Services,
and Mean Gross Charges per Family Incurring Gross Charges,
by Residence and Insurance Status

Residence and insurance status	Number of families	Mean gross charges per family	
		All families	Families incurring gross charges
All areas, total.................	2,809	$207	$225
Insured*.....................	1,780	$237	$251
Uninsured...................	1,029	154	176
Urban, areas of 1 million or more,			
total......................	773	237	259
Insured.....................	552	270	285
Uninsured...................	211	149	181
Other urban, total................	1,030	204	221
Insured.....................	698	232	248
Uninsured...................	332	144	161
Rural nonfarm, total.............	572	197	216
Insured.....................	326	212	225
Uninsured...................	246	177	204
Rural farm, total...............	434	178	190
Insured.....................	194	213	219
Uninsured...................	240	150	163

* An insured family is here defined as a family with hospital, surgical, or medical-
expense protection at the end of the survey year.

Table A-20. Mean Gross Hospital Charges per Family, and Mean Gross
Hospital Charges per Family Incurring Hospital Charges,
by Residence and Insurance Status

Residence and insurance status of family	Number of families	Mean gross hospital charges per family	
		All families	Families incurring gross hospital charges
All areas, total	2,809	$41	$158
Insured*	1,780	$49	$163
Uninsured	1,029	27	144
Urban, areas of 1 million or more, total	773	39	183
Insured	562	44	188
Uninsured	211	23	164
Other urban, total	1,030	44	164
Insured	698	53	169
Uninsured	332	25	144
Rural nonfarm, total	572	42	153
Insured	326	44	145
Uninsured	246	39	165
Rural farm, total	434	35	119
Insured	194	52	128
Uninsured	240	21	104

* An insured family is here defined as a family with hospital, surgical, or medical-expense protection at the end of the survey year.

Table A-21. Mean Gross Physicians' Charges per Family, and Mean Gross
Physicians' Charges per Family Incurring Gross Physicians' Charges,
by Residence and Insurance Status

Residence and insurance status	Number of families	Mean gross physicians' charges per family	
		All families	Families incurring gross physicians' charges
All areas, total..................	2,809	$78	$105
Insured*....................	1,780	$89	$111
Uninsured...................	1,029	61	93
Urban, areas of 1 million or more, total......................	773	91	125
Insured.....................	562	104	134
Uninsured...................	211	54	95
Other urban, total................	1,030	74	99
Insured.....................	698	82	103
Uninsured...................	332	56	90
Rural nonfarm, total.............	572	79	103
Insured.....................	326	83	103
Uninsured...................	246	73	102
Rural farm, total...............	434	69	88
Insured.....................	194	76	92
Uninsured...................	240	63	86

* An insured family is here defined as a family with hospital, surgical, or medical-
expense protection at the end of the survey year.

Table A-22. Mean Gross Medicines Charges per Family, and Mean Gross
Medicines Charges per Family Incurring Gross Medicines Charges,
by Residence and Insurance Status

Residence and insurance status	Number of families	Mean gross medicines charges per family	
		All families	Families incurring gross medicines charges
All areas, total.................	*2,809*	*$31*	*$46*
Insured*.....................	1,780	$33	$47
Uninsured...................	1,029	26	42
Urban, areas of 1 million or more,			
total......................	*773*	*32*	*48*
Insured.....................	562	36	50
Uninsured...................	211	22	39
Other urban, total...............	*1,030*	*29*	*42*
Insured.....................	698	31	43
Uninsured...................	332	24	38
Rural nonfarm, total............	*572*	*30*	*48*
Insured.....................	326	31	47
Uninsured...................	246	30	50
Rural farm, total...............	*434*	*33*	*49*
Insured.....................	194	39	54
Uninsured...................	240	28	44

* An insured family is here defined as a family with hospital, surgical, or medical-
expense protection at the end of the survey year.

Table A-23. Mean Gross "Other" Medical Charges per Family, and Mean Gross "Other" Medical Charges per Family Incurring Gross "Other" Medical Charges, by Residence and Insurance Status*

Residence and insurance status	Number of families	Mean other charges per family	
		All families	Families incurring other charges
All areas, total..................	2,809	$26	$54
Insured†....................	1,780	$29	$55
Uninsured...................	1,029	22	52
Urban, areas of 1 million or more,			
total.....................	773	27	58
Insured.....................	562	30	62
Uninsured...................	211	18	46
Other urban, total................	1,030	27	54
Insured.....................	698	29	53
Uninsured...................	332	23	55
Rural nonfarm, total.............	572	25	53
Insured.....................	326	27	51
Uninsured...................	246	23	57
Rural farm, total................	434	25	50
Insured.....................	194	26	51
Uninsured...................	240	25	49

* Gross "other" medical charges include medical appliances; ophthalmic products; services of oculists and optometrists; services of chiropractors, chiropodists, podiatrists, naturopaths, faith healers, etc.; the services of private-duty nurses, practical nurses, and midwives; and expenditures for laboratory services like diagnostic tests and X-rays for which the consumer was billed directly by the laboratory.

† An insured family is here defined as a family with hospital, surgical, or medical-expense protection at the end of the survey year.

Table A-24. Mean Dental Charges per Family, and Mean Dental Charges per Family Incurring Dental Charges, by Residence and Insurance Status

Residence and insurance status	Number of families	Mean dental charges per family	
		All families	Families incurring dental charges
All areas, total.................	*2,809*	*$33*	*$61*
Insured*.....................	1,780	$41	$68
Uninsured...................	1,029	20	46
Urban, areas of 1 million or more, total.....................	*773*	*51*	*91*
Insured.....................	562	70	97
Uninsured...................	211	32	71
Other urban, total...............	*1,030*	*31*	*57*
Insured.....................	698	37	60
Uninsured...................	332	20	46
Rural nonfarm, total............	*572*	*24*	*45*
Insured.....................	326	30	50
Uninsured...................	246	16	36
Rural farm, total...............	*434*	*19*	*37*
Insured.....................	194	27	42
Uninsured...................	240	13	31

* An insured family is here defined as a family with hospital, surgical, or medical-expense protection at the end of the survey year.

Table A-25. Percentage Distribution of Gross Total Costs, by Type of Service for Which Costs Were Incurred, for All Persons, by Family Income (Percentages may not add up to 100 because of rounding)

Type of service	Per cent distribution, by family income					
	All income groups (8,898 persons)	Under $2,000 (1,400 persons)	$2,000–$3,499 (1,917 persons)	$3,500–$4,999 (2,409 persons)	$5,000–$7,499 (1,956 persons)	$7,500 and over (1,171 persons)
Mean gross total costs*..	*$66*	*$54*	*$48*	*$61*	*$76*	*$102*
Hospital................	20⎫	21⎫	21⎫	20⎫	18⎫	18⎫
Surgery†..............	7⎪58	7⎪59	8⎪61	7⎪58	7⎪54	8⎪55
Obstetrics‡.............	4⎪	2⎪	5⎪	5⎪	3⎪	2⎪
Other physicians........	27⎭	29⎭	27⎭	26⎭	26⎭	27⎭
Medicines..............	15	20	15	14	15	11
"Other" medical........	12	11	13	12	13	13
Dental................	16	10	11	15	18	20

* Figures equal 100 %.

† Surgical costs are here defined as the fee charged by a physician or surgeon for a cutting procedure or the setting of a fracture. This may include preoperative and postoperative physicians' services, when the surgeon did not distinguish the charges for that care from the fee for the surgery. The charges for physicians assisting at the operation are also included here. The charges for the anesthetist, when not a hospital-staff member, are classified under *Other Physicians*. When the anesthetist's fee was included in the hospital bill, it was classified under *Hospitals*.

‡ Obstetrical costs are here defined as charges made by a physician for prenatal care, Cesarean and normal deliveries, and the care accompanying a miscarriage. Hospital charges connected with deliveries and miscarriages are included under *Hospital*, rather than here. Charges for medicines and tests connected with pregnancies are not classified here unless the physician billed the patient directly for these goods and services.

Table A-26. Percentage Distribution of Gross Total Costs, by Type of Service for Which Costs Were Incurred, for All Persons, by Insurance Status

Type of service	Per cent distribution, by insurance status		
	All persons (8,898)	Insured persons* (5,054)	Uninsured persons (3,844)
Mean gross charges†	*$66*	*$74*	*$55*
Hospital	20 ⎫	21 ⎫	17 ⎫
Surgery‡	7 ⎬ 58	8 ⎬ 59	6 ⎬ 56
Obstetrics§	4 ⎪	4 ⎪	4 ⎪
Other physicians	27 ⎭	26 ⎭	29 ⎭
Medicines	15	14	17
"Other" medical	12	12	14
Dental	16	17	14

* Insured persons are those with hospital insurance at the end of the survey year.

† Figures equal 100%.

‡ Surgical costs are here defined as the fee charged by a physician or surgeon for a cutting procedure or the setting of a fracture. This may include preoperative and postoperative physicians' services, when the surgeon did not distinguish the charges for that care from the fee for the surgery. The charges for physicians assisting at the operation are also included here. The charges for the anesthetist, when not a hospital-staff member, are classified under *Other Physicians*. When the anesthetist's fee was included in the hospital bill, it was classified under *Hospitals*.

§ Obstetrical costs are here defined as charges made by a physician for prenatal care, Cesarean and normal deliveries, and the care accompanying a miscarriage. Hospital charges connected with deliveries and miscarriages are included under *Hospital*, rather than here. Charges for medicines and tests connected with pregnancies are not classified here unless the physician billed the patient directly for these goods and services.

Table A-27. Mean Gross Total Charges per Person, and Mean Gross Total Charges per Person Incurring Gross Total Charges, by Age, Sex, and Insurance Status

Age and sex	Mean gross total charges per person					
	All persons			Persons incurring gross total charges		
	All	Insured	Unin-sured	All	Insured	Unin-sured
All persons (male and female), total........	$65	$74	$55	$ 94	$ 98	$ 87
Under 6*......	$ 28	$ 35	$ 20	$ 44	$ 48	$ 36
6–17..........	38	48	24	59	65	47
18–34........	70	84	51	98	108	80
35–54........	80	89	66	109	116	96
55–64........	96	106	85	131	142	117
65 and over...	102	111	98	140	140	141
Males, total......	*51*	*60*	*39*	*78*	*84*	*69*
Under 6*......	29	38	19	45	52	33
6–17..........	35	44	23	57	60	50
18–34........	43	56	27	71	82	54
35–54........	60	69	43	89	97	71
55–64........	88	105	66	127	147	99
65 and over...	77†	70†	80	115†	98†	124
Females, total....	*80*	*88*	*70*	*106*	*110*	*100*
Under 6*......	28	32	22	43	44	40
6–17..........	41	51	26	61	70	44
18–34........	94	106	75	114	123	98
35–54........	100	108	86	125	131	114
55–64........	104	108	100	134	137	130
65 and over...	124	158	112	161	181	152

* These means are slightly deflated by virtue of the fact that each child born during the survey year is treated as a "whole" person, i.e., counted as one in computing the mean for the year.

† The dip in charges for males after age 65 cannot be explained on any reasonable basis. Granted the adequacy of the method of collecting data, this seeming anomaly must stand as a simple fact. Unpublished data from insured families in Boston and Birmingham do not corroborate or deny the above pattern.

Table A-28. Mean Gross Hospital Charges per Person, and Mean Gross Hospital Charges per Person Incurring Gross Hospital Charges, by Age and Sex and Insurance Status

| Age and sex | Mean gross hospital charges per person | | | | | |
| | All persons | | | Persons incurring gross hospital charges | | |
	All	In-sured*	Unin-sured	All	Insured*	Uninsured
All persons (male and female), total.....	*$13*	*$16*	*$ 9*	*$140*	*$140*	*$142*
Under 6†..........	$ 5	$ 6	$ 2	$ 70	$ 72	$ 63
6–17..............	6	9	2	103	112	64
18–34.............	15	19	9	110	123	84
35–54.............	15	17	11	161	165	152
55–64.............	20	24	15	217	205	244
65 and over........	25	31	22	233	203	254
Males, total..........	*9*	*12*	*6*	*143*	*142*	*145*
Under 6†..........	5	7	2	71	73	62
6–17..............	6	9	2	95	102	68
18–34.............	5	8	1	124	139	66
35–54.............	12	14	9	176	179	166
55–64.............	18	24	10	240	261	190
65 and over........	16‡	16‡	17	176‡	131‡	211
Females, total..........	*17*	*20*	*13*	*139*	*138*	*140*
Under 6†..........	5	6	3	69	72	55
6–17..............	6	10	2	111	124	60
18–34.............	23	28	16	108	120	85
35–54.............	18	21	14	153	156	145
55–64.............	22	25	19	203	171	275
65 and over........	32	50	26	275	261	285

* Insured persons are persons with hospital insurance at end of the survey year.

† These means are slightly deflated by virtue of the fact that each child born during the survey year is treated as a "whole" person, i.e., counted as one in computing the mean for the year.

‡ The dip in charges for males after age 65 cannot be explained on any reasonable basis. Granted the adequacy of the method of collecting data, this seeming anomaly must stand as a simple fact. Unpublished data from insured families in Boston and Birmingham do not corroborate or deny the above pattern.

Table A-29. Mean Gross Physicians' Charges per Person, and Mean Gross
Physicians' Charges per Person Incurring Gross Physicians' Charges,
by Age and Sex and Insurance Status

	Mean gross physicians' charges per person					
	All persons			Persons incurring gross physicians' charges		
Age and sex	All	In-sured*	Unin-sured	All	In-sured*	Unin-sured
All persons (male and female), total...................	*$25*	*$38*	*$21*	*$57*	*$58*	*$57*
Under 6†.................	$15	$18	$11	$28	$30	$25
6–17......................	13	16	9	37	38	36
18–34....................	29	35	21	67	73	55
35–54....................	29	32	25	67	68	66
55–64....................	35	36	33	76	74	78
65 and over..............	36	36	36	74	65	78
Males, total.................	*19*	*22*	*15*	*51*	*51*	*49*
Under 6†.................	15	19	10	28	31	24
6–17......................	13	16	9	40	38	45
18–34....................	17	24	9	60	72	38
35–54....................	19	22	14	54	57	46
55–64....................	32	34	29	75	72	81
65 and over..............	30‡	27‡	32	68‡	54‡	77
Females, total................	*31*	*33*	*28*	*62*	*62*	*62*
Under 6†.................	15	16	12	28	29	26
6–17......................	13	16	9	35	38	30
18–34....................	39	44	33	70	74·	63
35–54....................	39	41	35	76	75	78
55–64....................	37	38	35	77	77	76
65 and over..............	41	47	39	78	77	79

* Insured persons are those with hospital insurance at end of survey year.

† These means are slightly deflated by virtue of the fact that each child born during the survey year is treated as a "whole" person, i.e., counted as one in computing the mean for the year.

‡ The dip in charges for males after age 65 cannot be explained on any reasonable basis. Granted the adequacy of the method of collecting data, this seeming anomaly must stand as a simple fact. Unpublished data from insured families in Boston and Birmingham do not corroborate or deny the above pattern.

Table A-30. Mean Gross Medicines Charges per Person, and Mean Gross
Medicines Charges per Person Incurring Gross Medicines Charges,
by Age and Sex and Insurance Status

Age and sex	Mean gross medicines charges per person					
	All persons			Persons incurring gross medicines charges		
	All	In-sured*	Unin-sured	All	In-sured*	Unin-sured
All persons (male and female), total	$10	$10	$ 9	$26	$25	$27
Under 6†	$ 6	$ 7	$ 5	$15	$15	$15
6–17	5	5	4	16	16	17
18–34	8	8	6	22	22	22
35–54	11	12	10	29	29	28
55–64	15	17	13	35	42	28
65 and over	22	23	21	42	40	42
Males, total	*7*	*8*	*6*	*23*	*23*	*23*
Under 6†	7	9	5	16	17	15
6–17	4	4	3	16	14	20
18–34	5	6	5	21	21	21
35–54	7	8	6	23	24	21
55–64	12	15	8	31	38	22
65 and over	17	17	16	37	38	36
Females, total	*12*	*12*	*12*	*28*	*26*	*29*
Under 6†	6	6	5	14	14	15
6–17	5	6	4	17	18	15
18–34	10	11	8	22	22	23
35–54	15	16	14	33	33	33
55–64	18	20	16	38	45	32
65 and over	26	29	25	45	43	46

* Insured persons are those with hospital insurance at end of survey year.

† These means are slightly deflated by virtue of the fact that each child born
during the survey year is treated as a "whole" person, i.e., counted as one in
computing the mean for the year.

Table A-31. Mean Gross "Other" Medical Charges per Person, and Mean Gross "Other" Medical Charges per Person Incurring Gross "Other" Medical Charges, by Age and Sex and Insurance Status

Age and sex	Mean gross "other" medical charges per person*					
	All persons			Persons incurring gross "other" medical charges		
	All	In- sured†	Unin- sured	All	In- sured†	Unin- sured
All persons (male and female), total.................	$ 8	$ 9	$ 7	$38	$38	$40
Under 6‡..............	$ 1	$ 1	$ 1	$22	$20	$24
6–17......................	4	4	3	26	26	26
18–34...................	7	7	6	32	31	33
35–54...................	11	13	8	39	41	35
55–64...................	15	15	14	45	44	47
65 and over..............	17	19	16	61	64	59
Males, total.................	*7*	*7*	*6*	*37*	*36*	*40*
Under 6‡..............	1	1	1	21	21	20
6–17......................	3	4	3	27	26	30
18–34...................	6	7	4	38	38	38
35–54...................	9	10	7	37	37	36
55–64...................	15	16	13	48	46	51
65 and over..............	11§	8§	12	46§	34§	52
Females, total.................	*9*	*10*	*9*	*39*	*39*	*39*
Under 6‡..............	1	1	1	23	19	31
6–17......................	4	5	4	25	26	24
18–34...................	7	8	7	29	28	31
35–54...................	13	16	10	41	45	34
55–64...................	15	15	16	43	42	45
65 and over..............	23	32	19	71	87	63

* Gross "other" medical charges include medical appliances; ophthalmic products; services of oculists and optometrists; services of chiropractors, chiropodists, podiatrists, naturopaths, faith healers, etc.; the services of private-duty nurses, practical nurses, and midwives; and expenditures for laboratory services like diagnostic tests and X-rays for which the consumer was billed directly by the laboratory.

† Insured persons are those with hospital insurance at end of survey year.

‡ These means are slightly deflated by virtue of the fact that each child born during the survey year is treated as a "whole" person, i.e., counted as one in computing the mean for the year.

§ The dip in charges for males after age 65 cannot be explained on any reasonable basis. Granted the adequacy of the method of collecting data, this seeming anomaly must stand as a simple fact. Unpublished data from insured families in Boston and Birmingham do not corroborate or deny the above pattern.

Table A-32. Mean Dental Charges per Person, and Mean Dental Charges per Person Incurring Dental Charges, by Age and Sex and Insurance Status

Age and sex	Mean dental charges per person					
	All persons			Persons incurring dental charges		
	All	In-sured*	Unin-sured	All	In-sured*	Unin-sured
All persons (male and female), total	$10	$12	$ 8	$32	$32	$32
Under 6†	$ 1	$ 2	‡	$16	$18	$10
6–17	11	13	$ 7	25	26	22
18–34	13	15	10	31	32	28
35–54	14	15	11	37	37	36
55–64	13	13	12	53	52	55
65 and over	4	3	5	37	24	43
Males, total	9	11	6	31	32	29
Under 6†	1	2	1	14	16	11
6–17	9	12	6	24	24	23
18–34	11	13	8	31	31	30
35–54	12	14	8	35	37	30
55–64	11	15	7	49	57	34
65 and over	5	3	6	43	36	47
Females, total	12	13	9	33	33	34
Under 6†	2	2	1	17	19	9
6–17	12	15	8	26	28	22
18–34	15	17	11	31	33	27
35–54	15	17	13	38	37	40
55–64	14	12	17	57	48	68
65 and over	3	2	4	31	12	39

* Insured persons are those with hospital insurance at the end of the survey year.

† These means are slightly deflated by virtue of the fact that each child born during the survey year is treated as a "whole" person, i.e., counted as one in computing the mean for the year.

‡ Fifty cents or less.

Table A-33. Mean Gross Total Charges per Person, and Mean Gross Charges per Person Incurring Charges, by Family Income and Insurance Status

Family income	Number of persons						Mean gross total charges per person					
	All persons			Persons incurring charges			All persons			Persons incurring charges		
	Total	In-sured	Unin-sured	Total	In-sured	Unin-sured	Total	In-sured	Unin-sured	Total	In-sured	Unin-sured
All income groups, total..............	8,898	5,054	3,844	6,230	3,814	2,416	$66	$74	$55	$94	$98	$87
Under $2,000........	1,400	359	1,041	840	223	607	54	75	47	90	115	81
$2,000-$3,499........	1,917	926	991	1,191	604	587	48	56	40	77	85	68
3,500- 4,999........	2,409	1,528	881	1,691	1,120	571	61	65	53	86	89	81
5,000- 7,499........	1,956	1,394	562	1,517	1,139	378	76	80	68	98	97	101
7,500 and over......	1,171	833	338	972	712	260	102	101	104	122	118	135

Table A-34. Mean Gross Charges per Person, and Mean Gross Charges per Person Incurring Gross Charges, by Income and Insurance Status

Per capita income	Number of persons						Mean gross total charges per person					
	All persons			Persons incurring charges			All persons			Persons incurring charges		
	Total	In-sured	Unin-sured	Total	In-sured	Unin-sured	Total	In-sured	Unin-sured	Total	In-sured	Unin-sured
All income groups*...	8,898	5,054	3,844	6,230	3,814	2,416	$66	$74	$55	$94	$98	$87
Under $500..........	1,378	428	950	675	216	459	33	40	29	66	78	61
$ 500-$ 999........	2,647	1,366	1,281	1,755	948	807	51	57	45	77	82	72
1,000– 1,499........	1,862	1,206	656	1,436	981	455	68	71	61	87	87	88
1,500– 1,999........	1,100	743	357	848	589	259	78	83	69	102	105	95
2,000– 2,499........	611	403	208	475	326	149	84	85	83	108	104	116
2,500 and over......	1,080	786	294	882	657	225	116	113	123	141	135	160

* Includes 122 insured persons and 98 uninsured persons in families with indeterminate per capita income. Fourteen insured persons were in families with indeterminate total family income; 31 uninsured persons were in such families. The remaining 175 persons were in families containing 5 or more individuals and with incomes of $10,000 or more. Since no attempt was made to collect detailed income information from families with incomes of $10,000 or more, it was impossible to classify the members of such families in terms of per capita income.

Table A-35. Percentage Distribution of Families, Persons, and Total Gross Charges, by Family Total Gross Charges, for Families Incurring Known Gross Charges*

Family total gross charges†	Number of families	Per cent of families with total gross charges	Per cent of total gross charges for families incurring given gross charges	Estimated national total gross charges, billions
All families, total...	2,754	100	*$570,000‡*	$10.2
None..............	224	8.2		
Under $46........	594	21.6	2.3	$0.2
$ 46–$ 94.....	439	15.8	5.2	0.5
95– 194.....	553	20.1	13.6	1.4
195– 294.....	324	11.8	13.7	1.4
295– 394.....	193	7.0	11.5	1.2
395– 494.....	136	4.9	10.5	1.1
495– 744.....	172	6.3	17.9	1.8
745– 994.....	65	2.3	9.7	1.0
995– 1,994......	42	1.6	9.4	1.0
1,995 and over....	12	0.4	6.2	0.6

* This table shows how unequally distributed personal health services charges are in a year. The fact that large families incur greater charges than small families does not account for this disproportion, since only 17.9% of the people in the sample were in these families.

† The 55 families with unknown gross charges are excluded from this table.

‡ Figure equals 100%.

Table A-36. Outlay for All Personal Health Services and for Voluntary Health Insurance, as a Percentage of Family Income

Outlay for health* as a percentage of family income	Number of families	Per cent of families
Total..	2,809	100
No outlay for health.............................	*131*	*5*
Some outlay for health............................	*2,678*	*95*
Under 5% of family income.......................	1,490	53
5–9% of family income...........................	630	22
10–19% of family income.........................	333	12
20–49% of family income.........................	131	5
50–99% of family income.........................	29	1
100% or over of family income....................	15	1
Per cent of family income unknown................	50	2
Median per cent for total outlay for health as a percentage of family income = 4.1%†		

* This figure, outlay for health, includes the net outlay figure *plus* amounts paid for voluntary health insurance. That is, net outlay is gross incurred charges *less* insurance benefits received and amounts still owed on these incurred charges *plus* payments made on old bills incurred prior to the survey year. Payments by the family for medical care of persons outside the family are included in "outlay for health."

† For half the families, the outlay for health amounted to less than 4.1% of family income; for the other half of the families, it amounted to more than 4.1% of family income.

Table A-37. Families with a High Percentage of Income Spent for
Personal Health Services

	Per cent of family income spent for personal health services		
	50% or more	20–49%	10–19%
Family income, total*..................	*44*	*131*	*333*
Under $1,000, %.....................	61	43	11
$1,000–$1,999, %....................	18	31	17
2,000– 3,499, %....................	14	12	27
3,500 and over, %.................	7	15	44
Per cent of the 2,758 families with known percentage of income spent, spending specified percentage of income.........	1.6	4.7	12.1

* Figures equal 100%.

While 74% of all families in the survey were headed by males under 65 years of age, only 36% of the families spending 50% or more of their incomes for medical care were so headed. Thirty per cent of the families spending 50% or more were headed by males 65 and over, the remaining 34% by females. Sixty-three per cent of the families spending between 20 and 49% of income were headed by males under 65.

While only 19% of all the families in the sample were one-person families or families composed only of one parent and his or her children, 43% of the families spending 50% or more of their incomes for medical care were of this composition. Thirty per cent of the families spending between 20 and 49% of income were of this composition.

While 43% of the entire sample claimed not to have enough liquid assets to pay for a $200 medical bill, 57% of the families spending 50% or more of their income claimed to have that little in liquid assets. Fifty-eight per cent of the families spending between 20 and 49% of their incomes claimed not to be able to pay a $200 medical bill out of their liquid assets.

Of the 903 families with incomes of $5,000 or greater, 7.6% spent between 10 and 19% of their incomes for medical care, 0.9% spent between 20 and 49%, and 0.2% spent 50% or more.

Table A-38. Percentage Distribution of Gross Charges for Personal Health Services among Families, by Type of Service

Gross charges	Per cent distribution, by type of service								
	All services	All physicians	Surgery	"Other" physicians	Obstetrical	Hospital	Medicines	"Other"	Dental
(2,809 = 100 %)									
No gross charges........	8	25	86	27	92	74	33	50	44
Under $46.............	21	30	3	36	1	4	46	33	35
$ 46–$ 94	16	17	3	18	3	7	12	11	10
95– 194..............	20	15	4	11	3	8	7	4	6
195 and over..........	34	11	3	6	*	6	2	2	4
Unknown..............	2	1	1	1	*	*	1	*	*

* Less than half of 1 %.

Table A-39. Percentage Distribution of Gross Total Charges among Families,
by Type of Service for Which Charges Were Incurred and
Level of Gross Charges Incurred
(Percentages may not add up to 100 because of rounding)

Type of service	Per cent distribution of charges			
	All families incurring known gross charges* (2,754)	Families incurring total gross charges of		
		$1–$94 (1,033 families)	$95–$394 (1,070 families)	$395 and over (427 families)
Mean gross total charges† . . .	*$205*	*$43*	*$207*	*$702*
Hospital.	19	2	12	27
Surgery‡.	7	1	4	11
Obstetrics§.	4	1	5	3
Other physicians.	26	34	28	24
Medicines.	15	22	16	13
"Other" medical.	13	22	13	11
Dental.	16	18	21	12

* Families with unknown gross total charges are excluded.

† Figures equal 100%.

‡ Surgical charges are here defined as the fee charged by a physician or surgeon for a cutting procedure or the setting of a fracture. This may include preoperative and postoperative physicians' services, when the surgeon did not distinguish the charges for that care from the fee for the surgery. The charges for physicians assisting at the operation are also included here. The charges for the anesthetist, when not a hospital-staff member, are classified under *Other Physicians.* When the anesthetist's fee was included in the hospital bill, it was classified under *Hospitals.*

§ Obstetrical charges are here defined as charges made by a physician for prenatal care, Cesarean and normal deliveries, and the care accompanying a miscarriage. Hospital charges connected with deliveries and miscarriages are included under *Hospital*, rather than here. Charges for medicines and tests connected with pregnancies are not classified here unless the physician billed the patient directly for these goods and services.

Table A-40. Percentage Distribution of Gross Hospital Charges among Families, by Family Income and Insurance Status

Family income	Number of families	Per cent reporting gross hospital charges* equal to					
		0	$1–$45	$46–$94	$95–$194	$195 and over	Amount unknown
All families (insured and uninsured), total..........	*2,809*	*74*	*4*	*7*	*8*	*6*	†
Under $2,000....	576	81	5	6	4	4	†
$2,000–$3,499...	613	75	5	7	8	5	†
3,500– 4,999...	699	72	4	8	10	5	†
5,000– 7,499...	566	71	4	8	9	7	1
7,500 and over..	337	71	4	4	11	10	0
Income unknown	18	‡	‡	‡	‡	‡	‡
Insured families, total..........	*1,780*	*70*	*4*	*8*	*10*	*7*	*1*
Under $2,000....	180	73	5	9	5	7	1
$2,000–$3,499...	345	70	4	8	10	6	1
3,500– 4,999...	520	70	4	8	11	6	1
5,000– 7,499...	458	70	4	8	9	7	1
7,500 and over..	272	70	4	4	12	10	0
Income unknown	5	‡	‡	‡	‡	‡	‡
Uninsured families, total..........	*1,029*	*81*	*4*	*6*	*5*	*4*	*0*
Under $2,000....	396	85	4	5	3	3	0
$2,000–$3,499...	268	81	5	5	5	4	0
3,500– 4,999...	179	79	4	7	6	3	0
5,000– 7,499...	108	76	1	9	9	5	0
7,500 and over..	65	75	4	4	7	10	0
Income unknown	13	‡	‡	‡	‡	‡	‡

* Gross hospital charges are the total amount of hospital bills. They include room-and-board charges, laboratory fees, drugs, X-rays, and the usual extras, but they do not include special nursing, the anesthetist's fee when anesthesia was administered by an outside anesthetist, or physicians' fees. These gross charges were mainly incurred in connection with inpatient care, but in a few instances they were for emergency outpatient care. Gross hospital charges exclude the "cost" of free care. (About 1 or 2% of families received only free hospital service.)

† Less than half of 1%.

‡ Percentages not computed for groups of less than 50 families.

Table A-41. Percentage Distribution of Gross Physicians' Charges among Families, by Family Income and Insurance Status

Family income	Number of families	Per cent reporting gross physicians' charges* equal to					
		0	$1–$45	$46–$94	$95–$194	$195 and over	Amount unknown
All families (insured and uninsured), total.........	*2,809*	*25*	*30*	*17*	*15*	*11*	*1*
Under $2,000....	576	37	30	17	10	5	1
$2,000–$3,499...	613	28	33	18	12	7	1
3,500– 4,999...	699	23	30	17	16	12	1
5,000– 7,499...	566	18	29	17	20	13	†
7,500 and over..	337	16	27	15	20	20	1
Income unknown	18	‡	‡	‡	‡	‡	‡
Insured families, total.........	*1,780*	*20*	*30*	*18*	*18*	*12*	*2*
Under $2,000....	180	28	30	20	12	7	3
$2,000–$3,499...	345	24	33	20	15	7	2
3,500– 4,999...	520	21	30	19	17	12	1
5,000– 7,499...	458	17	29	18	21	12	3
7,500 and over..	272	16	26	14	23	20	1
Income unknown	5	‡	‡	‡	‡	‡	‡
Uninsured families, total.........	*1,029*	*34*	*31*	*15*	*10*	*9*	†
Under $2,000....	396	41	30	16	9	4	†
$2,000–$3,499...	268	34	34	16	9	6	†
3,500– 4,999...	179	30	30	12	15	13	1
5,000– 7,499...	108	26	30	16	12	16	0
7,500 and over..	65	17	31	20	10	21	1
Income unknown	13	‡	‡	‡	‡	‡	‡

* Gross physicians' charges are all charges *made by physicians* (or clinics) for medical goods and services. They include voluntary health insurance benefits received by the physician or by the family to cover these charges, but they exclude the "cost" of free care.

† Less than half of 1%.

‡ Percentages not computed for groups of less than 50 families.

Table A-42. Percentage Distribution of Gross Surgical Charges among Families, by Family Income and Insurance Status

Family income	Number of families	Per cent reporting gross surgical charges* equal to					
		0	$1–$45	$46–$94	$95–$194	$195 and over	Amount unknown
All families (insured and uninsured), total	*2,809*	*86*	*3*	*3*	*4*	*3*	*1*
Under $2,000....	576	92	2	2	3	1	1
$2,000–$3,499...	613	87	3	4	3	2	1
3,500– 4,999...	699	86	5	2	3	3	1
5,000– 7,499...	566	82	5	5	5	2	1
7,500 and over..	337	83	1	4	6	5	1
Income unknown	18	‡	‡	‡	‡	‡	‡
Insured families, total	*1,780*	*83*	*4*	*4*	*5*	*3*	*1*
Under $2,000....	180	84	3	3	6	2	2
$2,000–$3,499...	345	84	4	5	3	3	1
3,500– 4,999...	520	84	6	3	4	3	1
5,000– 7,499...	458	80	5	5	6	3	2
7,500 and over..	272	82	1	5	6	5	†
Income unknown	5	‡	‡	‡	‡	‡	‡
Uninsured families, total	*1,029*	*92*	*2*	*1*	*3*	*2*	†
Under $2,000....	396	95	1	1	2	1	0
$2,000–$3,499...	268	91	2	2	3	1	†
3,500– 4,999...	179	91	2	1	1	4	1
5,000– 7,499...	108	88	5	2	4	2	0
7,500 and over..	65	85	1	1	7	4	1
Income unknown	13	‡	‡	‡	‡	‡	‡

* Gross surgical charges are all physicians' fees for surgical procedures, which are defined here to include the treatment of fractures and dislocations and all "cutting" procedures with the exception of deliveries by Cesarean. The cost of Cesarean deliveries is included under obstetrical costs. The figures do not include the "cost" of free surgical care, but they do include surgical insurance benefits paid to the physician or to the patient.

† Less than half of 1%.

‡ Percentages not computed for groups of less than 50 families.

Table A-43. Percentage Distribution of Gross Obstetrical Charges among Families, by Family Income and Insurance Status

Family income	Number of families	Per cent reporting gross obstetrical charges* equal to					
		0	$1–$45	$46–$94	$95–$194	$195 and over	Amount unknown
All families (insured and uninsured), total...........	2,809	92	1	3	3	†	†
Under $2,000....	576	95	2	3	1	0	0
$2,000–$3,499...	613	92	1	4	3	†	†
3,500– 4,999...	699	89	2	3	5	1	0
5,000– 7,499...	566	92	1	2	4	1	0
7,500 and over..	337	95	1	1	2	1	0
Income unknown	18	‡	‡	‡	‡	‡	0
Insured families, total...........	1,780	92	1	3	4	1	†
Under $2,000....	180	97	1	1	1	0	0
$2,000–$3,499...	345	91	1	3	4	†	†
3,500– 4,999...	520	89	2	4	5	1	0
5,000– 7,499...	458	92	1	2	4	†	0
7,500 and over..	272	96	0	1	2	1	0
Income unknown	5	‡	‡	‡	‡	‡	‡
Uninsured families, total...........	1,029	92	1	4	2	†	0
Under $2,000....	396	93	2	4	1	0	0
$2,000–$3,499...	268	93	1	5	1	0	0
3,500– 4,999...	179	91	1	2	5	1	0
5,000– 7,499...	108	90	1	4	5	1	0
7,500 and over..	65	92	3	1	1	3	0
Income unknown	13	‡	‡	‡	‡	‡	0

* Gross obstetrical charges are all physicians' charges associated with pregnancies. It includes both prenatal care and delivery (including charge for Cesarean deliveries). Frequently, where the mother was currently pregnant, her arrangement with the doctor was such that she would be billed a single amount for prenatal care and delivery. In such cases no charges were allocated to prenatal care already received. This was compensated for by the corollary case where the baby was born early in the survey year and the charges for prenatal care received prior to the survey year included in the survey year charges.

† Less than half of 1%.

‡ Percentages not computed for groups of less than 50 families.

Table A-44. Percentage Distribution of Gross "Other" Physicians' Charges
among Families by Family Income and Insurance Status

Family income	Number of families	Per cent reporting gross "other" physicians' charges* equal to					
		0	$1–$45	$46–$94	$95–$194	$195 and over	Amount unknown
All families (insured and uninsured), total..........	2,809	27	36	18	11	6	1
Under $2,000....	576	40	33	16	8	3	1
$2,000–$3,499...	613	31	40	17	7	4	1
3,500– 4,999...	699	25	37	20	12	6	1
5,000– 7,499...	566	20	36	20	14	8	2
7,500 and over..	337	17	33	18	19	11	1
Income unknown	18	‡	‡	‡	‡	‡	‡
Insured families, total..........	1,780	22	37	21	13	6	1
Under $2,000....	180	30	35	21	9	2	2
$2,000–$3,499...	345	27	40	19	8	3	1
3,500– 4,999...	520	22	38	22	11	5	1
5,000– 7,499...	458	18	36	21	15	7	2
7,500 and over..	272	17	33	18	21	11	1
Income unknown	5	‡	‡	‡	‡	‡	‡
Uninsured families, total..........	1,029	36	35	15	9	5	†
Under $2,000....	396	44	32	13	7	3	†
$2,000–$3,499...	268	35	40	14	6	4	1
3,500– 4,999...	179	32	35	14	12	7	0
5,000– 7,499...	108	30	33	19	9	9	0
7,500 and over..	65	20	34	20	14	11	1
Income unknown	13	‡	‡	‡	‡	‡	‡

* Gross "other" physicians' charges are all physicians' charges except charges
for surgical or obstetrical care. It includes insurance benefits received to cover
gross "other" physicians' charges, but it excludes the "cost" of free care.

† Less than half of 1%.

‡ Percentages not computed for groups of less than 50 families.

Table A-45. Percentage Distribution of Gross Medicines Charges among Families by Family Income and Insurance Status

Family income	Number of families	Per cent reporting gross medicines charges* equal to					
		0	$1–$45	$46–$94	$95–$194	$195 and over	Amount unknown
All families (insured and uninsured), total	*2,809*	*33*	*46*	*12*	*7*	*2*	*1*
Under $2,000....	576	38	44	9	6	1	1
$2,000–$3,499...	613	39	46	10	3	1	†
3,500– 4,999...	699	31	47	13	7	1	†
5,000– 7,499...	566	26	48	12	9	3	1
7,500 and over..	337	26	43	20	8	2	†
Income unknown	18	‡	‡	‡	‡	‡	‡
Insured families, total	*1,780*	*29*	*47*	*14*	*7*	*2*	†
Under $2,000....	180	31	49	9	9	1	1
$2,000–$3,499...	345	37	47	10	4	1	1
3,500– 4,999...	520	30	46	15	7	1	†
5,000– 7,499...	458	26	48	14	9	4	†
7,500 and over..	272	24	44	21	8	3	0
Income unknown	5	‡	‡	‡	‡	‡	‡
Uninsured families, total	*1,029*	*38*	*44*	*10*	*5*	*2*	*1*
Under $2,000....	396	41	42	10	5	2	1
$2,000–$3,499...	268	42	46	9	2	1	†
3,500– 4,999...	179	34	48	9	7	2	1
5,000– 7,499...	108	29	48	8	11	3	2
7,500 and over..	65	32	41	15	8	1	1
Income unknown	13	‡	‡	‡	‡	‡	‡

* Gross medicines charges refers to the charges for medicines (either prescriptions or other drugs and medicines) which the family bought from the drug store or elsewhere rather than medicines which a hospital patient received and for which he was billed on the hospital bill. Similarly, it does not include medicines which the doctor administered to the patient and charged for on the doctor bill.

† Less than half of 1%.

‡ Percentages not computed for groups of less than 50 families.

Table A-46. Percentage Distribution of Gross "Other" Charges among Families, by Family Income and Insurance Status

Family income	Number of families	Per cent reporting gross "other" charges* equal to					
		0	$1–$45	$46–$94	$95–$194	$195 and over	Amount unknown
All families (insured and uninsured), total.........	*2,809*	*50*	*33*	*11*	*4*	*2*	†
Under $2,000....	576	62	26	8	2	1	†
$2,000–$3,499...	613	57	30	9	2	2	†
3,500– 4,999...	699	51	34	11	3	1	†
5,000– 7,499...	566	40	39	13	6	3	†
7,500 and over..	337	33	38	18	7	3	†
Income unknown	18	‡	‡	‡	‡	‡	‡
Insured families, total.........	*1,780*	*45*	*37*	*12*	*4*	*2*	†
Under $2,000....	180	56	30	11	2	1	1
$2,000–$3,499...	345	55	33	8	3	1	0
3,500– 4,999...	520	48	37	11	3	1	†
5,000– 7,499...	458	38	41	13	6	2	†
7,500 and over..	272	33	39	18	7	3	0
Income unknown	5	‡	‡	‡	‡	‡	‡
Uninsured families, total.........	*1,029*	*59*	*26*	*10*	*3*	*2*	†
Under $2,000....	396	65	24	7	2	1	†
$2,000–$3,499...	268	60	27	10	1	3	†
3,500– 4,999...	179	60	27	9	2	1	0
5,000– 7,499...	108	49	31	13	5	4	0
7,500 and over..	65	32	31	20	10	6	1
Income unknown	13	‡	‡	‡	‡	‡	‡

* Gross "other" charges include medical appliances; ophthalmic products; services of oculists and optometrists; services of chiropractors, chiropodists, podiatrists, naturopaths, faith healers, etc.; the services of private-duty nurses, practical nurses, and midwives; and expenditure for laboratory services like diagnostic tests and X-rays for which the consumer was billed directly by the laboratory.

† Less than half of 1%.

‡ Percentages not computed for groups of less than 50 families.

Table A-47. Percentage Distribution of Dental Charges among Families,
by Family Income and Insurance Status

Family income	Number of families	Per cent reporting dental charges* equal to					
		0	$1–$45	$46–$94	$95–$194	$195 and over	Amount unknown
All families (insured and uninsured), total..........	*2,809*	*44*	*35*	*10*	*6*	*4*	†
Under $2,000....	576	70	22	4	2	1	0
$2,000–$3,499...	613	56	32	7	3	1	†
3,500– 4,999...	699	37	43	9	7	3	†
5,000– 7,499...	566	29	38	15	11	6	†
7,500 and over..	337	22	36	20	10	10	1
Income unknown	18	‡	‡	‡	‡	‡	‡
Insured families, total..........	*1,780*	*37*	*37*	*12*	*8*	*5*	†
Under $2,000....	180	62	26	7	3	1	0
$2,000–$3,499...	345	52	34	9	3	2	0
3,500– 4,999...	520	35	44	9	8	4	†
5,000– 7,499...	458	29	36	15	13	6	†
7,500 and over..	272	20	36	22	10	11	1
Income unknown	5	‡	‡	‡	‡	‡	‡
Uninsured families, total..........	*1,029*	*56*	*31*	*7*	*3*	*2*	†
Under $2,000....	396	73	21	3	2	2	0
$2,000–$3,499...	268	60	30	6	3	1	†
3,500– 4,999...	179	42	43	8	5	2	0
5,000– 7,499...	108	32	43	16	5	3	0
7,500 and over..	65	31	39	13	10	7	0
Income unknown	13	‡	‡	‡	‡	‡	‡

* Dental charges are all charges by dentists for their services and any dental laboratory work.

† Less than half of 1%.

‡ Percentages not computed for groups of less than 50 families.

Table A-48. Percentage Distribution of Families, by Gross Charges for
All Personal Health Services and Residence
(Percentages may not add up to 100 because of rounding)

Gross charges for all personal health services	Per cent distribution, by residence				
	All areas (2,809* families)	Urban, areas of 1 million or more (773* families)	Other urban (1,030* families)	Rural nonfarm (572* families)	Rural farm (434* families)
No gross charges........	8	8	8	9	6
Under $46..............	21	18	20	23	27
$ 46–$ 94..............	16	15	15	17	16
95– 194..............	20	20	21	18	18
195 and over...........	34	36	34	30	32
Unknown...............	2	2	2	3	1

* Figures equal 100%.

Table A-49. Percentage Distribution of Families, by Gross Physicians'
Charges and Residence
(Percentages may not add up to 100 because of rounding)

Gross physicians' charges	Per cent distribution, by residence				
	All areas (2,809* families)	Urban, areas of 1 million or more (773* families)	Other urban (1,030* families)	Rural nonfarm (572* families)	Rural farm (434* families)
No gross physicians' charges	25	28	26	23	22
Under $46	30	26	30	31	35
$ 46–$ 94	17	16	18	18	16
95– 194	15	16	14	14	17
195 and over	11	12	10	11	9
Unknown	1	1	1	3	1

* Figures equal 100%.

Table A-50. Percentage Distribution of Families, by Gross Hospital
Charges and Residence
(Percentages may not add up to 100 because of rounding)

Gross hospital charges	Per cent distribution, by residence				
	All areas (2,809* families)	Urban, areas of 1 million or more (773* families)	Other urban (1,030* families)	Rural nonfarm (572* families)	Rural farm (434* families)
No gross hospital charges.	74	79	73	73	71
Under $46..............	4	2	4	5	7
$ 46–$ 94..............	7	4	8	8	9
95– 194..............	8	8	9	7	8
195 and over..........	6	6	6	6	5
Unknown..............	†	†	†	†	†

* Figures equal 100%.
† Less than half of 1%.

Table A-51. Percentage Distribution of Families, by Gross Medicines
Charges and Residence
(Percentages may not add up to 100 because of rounding)

Gross medicines charges*	Per cent distribution, by residence				
	All areas (2,809† families)	Urban, areas of 1 million or more (773† families)	Other urban (1,030† families)	Rural nonfarm (572† families)	Rural farm (434† families)
No gross medicines charges...............	33	32	31	36	32
Under $46..............	46	46	47	43	48
$ 46–$ 94..............	12	12	14	12	9
95– 194..............	7	8	5	5	9
195 and over...........	2	2	2	3	1
Unknown..............	1	1	‡	1	‡

* Gross medicines charges refer to the charges for medicines (either prescriptions or other drugs and medicines) which the family bought from the drugstore or elsewhere, other than medicines which a hospital patient received and for which he was billed on the hospital bill. Similarly, it does not include medicines which the physician administered to the patient and charged for on the physician's bill.

† Figures equal 100%.

‡ Less than half of 1%.

Table A-52. Percentage Distribution of Persons, by Level of Gross Total Charges
for All Personal Health Services, by Age
(Percentages may not add up to 100 because of rounding)

Gross total charges	Per cent distribution, by age						
	All persons (8,898*)	Under 6 (1,177* persons)	6–17 (1,852* persons)	18–34 (1,959* persons)	35–54 (2,336* persons)	55–64 (780* persons)	65 and over (767* persons)
No gross charges.....	30	35	36	28	26	26	28
Under $46..........	38	47	43	37	36	32	32
$ 46–$ 94..........	14	10	11	13	16	17	17
95– 194..........	10	6	7	11	11	11	11
195 and over.......	8	2	4	11	11	13	13
Gross charges unknown........	†	†	†	†	†	†	†

* Figures equal 100 %.
† Half, or less than half, of 1%.

Table A-53. Percentage Distribution of Persons, by Level of
Gross Hospital Charges and Age
(Percentages may not add up to 100 because of rounding)

Gross hospital charges	All persons (8,898*)	Per cent distribution, by age					
		Under 6 (1,177* persons)	6–17 (1,852* persons)	18–34 (1,959* persons)	35–54 (1,495* persons)	55–64 (780* persons)	65 and over (767* persons)
No gross charges.....	91	93	94	87	90	91	89
Under $46..........	2	3	2	2	1	1	1
$ 46–$ 94..........	3	2	2	5	3	1	2
95– 194..........	3	1	2	5	3	3	3
195 and over.......	2	†	†	1	2	4	3
Gross hospital charges unknown........	†	†	†	†	†	†	†

* Figures equal 100%.
† Half, or less than half, of 1%.

Table A-54. Percentage Distribution of Persons, by Level of
Gross Physicians' Charges, by Age
(Percentages may not add up to 100 because of rounding)

Gross physicians' charges	Per cent distribution, by age						
	All persons (8,898*)	Under 6 (1,177* persons)	6–17 (1,852* persons)	18–34 (1,959* persons)	35–54 (2,336* persons)	55–64 (780* persons)	65 and over (767* persons)
No gross charges.....	56	46	65	57	56	54	51
Under $46..........	28	45	27	25	26	25	26
$ 46–$ 94..........	8	6	5	8	8	9	12
95– 194..........	5	2	3	7	6	6	6
195 and over.......	2	†	1	3	4	5	4
Gross charges unknown.........	†	†	†	†	†	†	†

* Figures equal 100%.
† Half, or less than half, of 1%.

Table A-55. Percentage Distribution of Individuals by Level of Gross Surgical Charges for Individuals Grouped According to Whether or Not They Were Covered by Surgical Insurance at the Time of Surgery*

Level of gross surgical charges	Individuals incurring some gross surgical charges, % (434‡)	Individuals covered by surgical insurance at time of surgery and incurring gross surgical charges,† % (273‡)	Individuals not covered by surgical insurance at time of surgery and incurring gross surgical charges,† % (161‡)
Under $26...........	20	20	20
$ 26–$ 45...........	13	14	12
46– 94...........	21	22	20
95– 145...........	16	16	17
146– 195...........	12	12	11
196– 295...........	10	10	10
296 and over.......	5	4	7
Indeterminate.......	3	2	3
Mean per individual with some gross surgical charges....	$101	$96	$110
Median for those with some gross surgical charges..........	$69	$63	$76

* Individuals upon whom surgical procedures were performed but who did not incur any gross surgical costs (Veterans Administration, welfare cases, professional courtesy, workmen's compensation, etc.) are excluded from all parts of this table.

† See the fourth footnote to Table A-1 for basis of classification in terms of surgical-insurance coverage.

‡ Figures equal 100%.

Table A-56. Percentage of Families with Some Outstanding Medical Indebtedness*
at End of the Survey Year, by Family Income and Insurance Status

Income	Per cent with some outstanding medical indebtedness†		
	All families (2,809)	With insurance (1,780)	Without insurance (1,029)
All income groups..........	15	15	15
Under $2,000..............	16	15	16
$2,000–$3,499..............	17	18	14
3,500– 4,999..............	17	17	15
5,000– 7,499..............	13	12	15
7,500 and over...........	8	8	8

* In no instances did the amount unknown exceed 1%.

† Outstanding medical indebtedness includes debts owed to hospitals, physicians, dentists, and other suppliers of medical goods and services at the end of the survey year *less* any amount which the family planned to pay on such bills during the month following the interview.

Table A-57. Percentage of Families with Outstanding Medical Indebtedness under $95* at the End of the Survey Year, by Family Income and Insurance Status

Income	Per cent with outstanding medical indebtedness† under $95		
	All families (2,809)	With insurance (1,780)	Without insurance (1,029)
All income groups..........	9	10	9
Under $2,000..............	13	12	14
$2,000–$3,499..............	10	12	9
3,500– 4,999..............	10	12	5
5,000– 7,499..............	7	7	8
7,500 and over............	4	4	1

* In no instances did the amount unknown exceed 1%.

† For definition of indebtedness, see second footnote to Table A-56.

Table A-58. Percentage of Families with Outstanding Medical Indebtedness from $95 to $194* at the End of the Survey Year, by Family Income and Insurance Status

Income	Per cent with outstanding medical indebtedness† from $95 to $194		
	All families (2,809)	With insurance (1,780)	Without insurance (1,029)
All income groups..........	3	3	3
Under $2,000..............	1	1	1
$2,000–$3,499..............	3	4	3
3,500– 4,999..............	4	3	4
5,000– 7,499..............	2	2	3
7,500 and over............	2	1	6

* In no instances did the amount unknown exceed 1%.
† For definition of indebtedness, see second footnote to Table A-56.

Table A-59. Percentage of Families with Outstanding Medical Indebtedness of $195 and Over* at the End of the Survey Year, by Family Income and Insurance Status

Income	Per cent with outstanding medical indebtedness† of $195 and over		
	All families (2,809)	With insurance (1,780)	Without insurance (1,029)
All income groups..........	2	2	3
Under $2,000..............	2	1	2
$2,000–$3,499.............	2	2	2
3,500– 4,999.............	2	2	4
5,000– 7,499.............	3	3	4
7,500 and over...........	2	2	1

* In no instances did the amount unknown exceed 1%.
† For definition of indebtedness, see second footnote to Table A-56.

Table A-60. Number of Families Reporting Borrowing during the Survey Year
to Pay for Personal Health Services, by Source of Funds, and
Average and Median Amounts Borrowed

Source of funds	Number of families borrowing	Amount borrowed	
		Average	Median
Total..........................	120	$212	$150
Financial institutions*..........	77	248	170
Individuals....................	39	143	62
Source unknown...............	4		

* Includes banks, small-loan companies, credit unions, and, in three instances,
life-insurance companies.

Table A-61. Families Reporting Medical Indebtedness, by Family Income and Percentage of Income Paid Out for Health

Family income and per cent of income paid out for health*	Number of families	Families reporting outstanding medical indebtedness,† %
Total, all income groups...	*2,809*	*15*
Under 5%.............	1,624	9
5–9%................	626	19
10–14%..............	222	24
15% or more...........	286	28
Per cent unknown.......	51	‡
Under $2,000.............	*576*	*16*
Under 5%.............	241	10
5–9%................	103	14
10–14%..............	59	12
15% or more...........	167	27
Per cent unknown.......	6	‡
$2,000–$3,499............	*613*	*17*
Under 5%.............	351	10
5–9%................	141	26
10–14%..............	62	18
15% or more...........	50	27
Per cent unknown.......	9	‡
$3,500–$4,999............	*699*	*17*
Under 5%.............	415	11
5–9%................	187	19
10–14%..............	51	37
15% or more...........	40	‡
Per cent unknown.......	6	‡
$5,000 plus..............	*903*	*11*
Under 5%.............	614	7
5–9%................	195	16
10–14%..............	50	30
15% or more...........	29	‡
Per cent unknown.......	15	‡
Income unknown.........	*18*	‡

* The amount of income paid out for health is net outlay *plus* amount *paid by the family* for hospital, surgical, or medical expense insurance. Net outlay excludes benefits received from hospital, surgical, or medical expense insurance.

† For definition of indebtedness see second footnote to Table A-56.

‡ This percentage has not been computed for groups of under 50 families.

Table A-62. Families Reporting Outstanding Medical Indebtedness,
by Type of Family and by Insurance Status

Type of family	Number of families			Families reporting indebtedness,* %		
	Total	With insurance	With no insurance	All families	With insurance	With no insurance
Total, all types...........	2,809	1,780	1,029	15	15	15
Single-person families.....	387	172	215	6	5	7
Married couples, no children under 18.......	905	588	317	9	7	11
Married couples, with children under 18.......	1,271	879	392	21	21	21
Other types of families....	246	141	105	18	18	18

* For definition of indebtedness see second footnote to Table A-56.

Table A-63. Percentage of Families Reporting Borrowing to Pay for Personal Health Services, by Family Income and Insurance Status

Family income	Number of families	Families reporting borrowing,* %
All families (insured and uninsured), total........	*2,809*	*4*
Under $2,000...............................	576	5
$2,000–$3,499.............................	613	4
3,500– 4,999.............................	699	6
5,000– 7,499.............................	566	3
7,500 and over...........................	337	1
Income unknown...........................	18	†
Families with insurance, total....................	*1,780*	*4*
Under $2,000...............................	180	5
$2,000–$3,499.............................	345	5
3,500– 4,999.............................	520	7
5,000– 7,499.............................	458	2
7,500 and over...........................	272	1
Income unknown...........................	5	†
Families with no insurance, total................	*1,029*	*4*
Under $2,000...............................	396	5
$2,000–$3,499.............................	268	3
3,500– 4,999.............................	179	5
5,000– 7,499.............................	108	4
7,500 and over...........................	65	1
Income unknown...........................	13	†

* Included here are families who reported borrowing money during the survey year from regular lending institutions, friends, relatives, or any other source, for the express purpose of paying for personal health services.

† Percentages not computed for groups of less than 50 families.

Table A-64. Percentage of Families Reporting Borrowing to Meet Charges for Personal Health Services, by Size of Family

Size of family	Number of families	Families reporting borrowing,* %
Total, all sizes................	2,809	4
Single-person families.........	387	2
Two-person families...........	829	3
Three-person families.........	553	3
Four-person families..........	510	6
Five-person families..........	291	7
Six or more persons...........	239	10

* Included here are families who reported borrowing money during the survey year from regular lending institutions, friends, relatives, or any other source, for the express purpose of paying for personal health services.

Table A-65. Percentage of Families Reporting Borrowing to Meet Charges for Personal Health Services, by Percentage of Family Income Paid Out for Health

Per cent of income paid out for health*	Number of families	Families reporting borrowing,† %
Total..........................	2,809	4
Under 5%.....................	1,624	1
5–9%..........................	626	5
10–19%.......................	332	12
20–39%.......................	104	21
40% or more.................	72	18
Per cent unknown............	51	10

* The amount of income paid out for health is net outlay *plus* amounts *paid by the family* for voluntary health insurance. Net outlay excludes hospital, surgical, and medical insurance benefits.

† Included here are families who reported borrowing money during the survey year from regular lending institutions, friends, relatives, or any other source, for the express purpose of paying for personal health services.

Table A-66. Mean Insurance Benefits per Family and Total Insurance Benefits
as a Percentage of Total Gross Charges, for Insured Families,
by Their Total Gross Charges*

Family total gross charges	Number of insured families†	Mean insurance benefits (averaged over *all* insured families with given total gross charges)	Total insurance benefits, as % of total gross charges for insured families incurring given total gross charges
All insured families...	1,733	$ 45	19
None..............	98		
Under $46..........	290	2	8
$ 46–$ 94..........	256	4	6
95– 194..........	393	16	11
195– 294..........	242	33	14
295– 394..........	136	67	20
395– 494..........	103	100	23
495– 744..........	126	147	25
745– 994..........	47	204	24
995 and over.......	42	362	23

* Forty-five insured families with unknown gross charges and two insured families with known gross charges but unknown net charges are excluded from this table.

† An insured family is here defined as a family in which at least one individual was covered by some form of voluntary health insurance.

Table A-67. Percentage of Families Receiving Insurance Benefits and
Mean Insurance Benefits Received per Family Receiving Benefits,
for Insured Families, by Their Total Gross Charges

Family total gross charges	Number of insured families*	Insured families receiving some insurance benefits, %	Mean benefits received per family receiving some insurance benefits
All insured families.......	1,780	33	$144†
None..................	98		
Under $46..............	290	9	20
$ 46–$ 94..............	256	13	32
95– 194..............	393	27	59
195– 294..............	242	38	87
295– 394..............	136	51	131
395– 494..............	103	68	147
495– 744..............	126	70	210
745– 994..............	47	66	309
995 and over..........	42	74	490
Gross or net charges unknown..............	47	81	‡

* An insured family is here defined as a family in which at least one individual
was covered by some form of voluntary health insurance.

† Insurance benefits received by families with either unknown gross or unknown
net charges are excluded from this mean.

‡ Indeterminate.

Table A-68. Mean Insurance Benefits Received per Person and per Person Receiving Benefits, by Age and Sex

Age and sex	Mean insurance benefits received	
	Per person	Per person receiving benefits
All insured persons (males and females), total.	*$17*	*$116*
Under 6*.............................	$ 7	$ 55
6–17................................	11	98
18–34...............................	21	123
35–54...............................	19	126
55–64...............................	25	149
65 and over.........................	28	150
Insured males, total...................	*13*	*102*
Under 6*.............................	9	59
6–17................................	12	92
18–34...............................	8	91
35–54...............................	16	115
55–64...............................	26	161
65 and over.........................	17	102
Insured females, total.................	*21*	*126*
Under 6*.............................	6	51
6–17................................	10	105
18–34...............................	31	132
35–54...............................	23	135
55–64...............................	24	139
65 and over.........................	41	195

* These means are slightly deflated by virtue of the fact that each child born during the survey year is treated as a "whole" person, i.e., counted as one in computing the mean for the year.

Table A-69. Percentage of Families with Specified Percentage of Gross Charges Met by Insurance Benefits, for Insured Families, by Levels of Gross Charges Incurred

Family total gross charges incurred	Number of insured families	Some benefits received, %	Per cent of families, by per cent of gross charges met				
			20 % or more	40 % or more	50 % or more	60 % or more	80 % or more
All insured families*........	1,733	32	22	13	8	6	2
All insured families with some gross charges*...	1,635	33	24	13	9	6	3
None.............	98						
Under $46........	290	9	8	5	4	4	4
$ 46–$ 94........	256	13	9	6	5	3	2
95– 194........	393	27	20	11	6	5	2
195– 294........	242	38	26	14	10	7	2
295– 394........	136	51	37	25	16	11	4
395– 494........	103	68	45	21	13	8	3
495– 744........	126	70	47 ⎫	28 ⎫	21 ⎫	13 ⎫	2 ⎫
745– 994........	47	66	57 ⎬ 49 %	28 ⎬ 27 %	19 ⎬ 19 %	6 ⎬ 10 %	2 ⎬ 2 %
995 and over......	42	74	45 ⎭	24 ⎭	12 ⎭	5 ⎭	2 ⎭

* Forty-five insured families with unknown gross charges and two insured families with known gross charges but unknown net charges are excluded from this total.

Table A-70. Percentage of Families with Specified Percentage of Gross Charges
Met by Insurance Benefits, for Insured Families Who Received Benefits,
by Levels of Gross Charges Incurred

Family total gross charges incurred	Number of insured families who received benefits	Per cent of families, by per cent of gross charges met				
		20% or more	40% or more	50% or more	60% or more	80% or more
All insured families who received benefits*........	546	71	40	27	18	8
Under $46........	26	88	54	46	46	42
$ 46–$ 94........	33	73	45	36	24	12
95– 194........	105	73	40	23	17	9
195– 294........	92	67	37	26	20	5
295– 394........	70	71	49	31	21	7
395– 494........	70	66	31	19	11	4
495– 744........	88	67⎫	39⎫	30⎫	19⎫	2⎫
745– 994........	31	87⎬70	42⎬38	29⎬27	10⎬15	3⎬3
995 and over.....	31	61⎭	32⎭	16⎭	6⎭	3⎭

* Thirty-eight families with unknown gross or net charges who received insurance
benefits are completely excluded from this total.

Table A-71. Total Insurance Benefits as a Percentage of Total Gross Charges, for Insured Families, by Specified Levels of Gross Charges Incurred and by Income

Income	Number of insured families incurring some gross charges*	Total insurance benefits as % of total gross charges of insured families incurring some gross charges*
All income groups......	1,637	19
Under $2,000..........	158	26
$2,000–$3,499..........	304	20
3,500– 4,999..........	481	22
5,000– 7,499..........	432	18
7,500 and over........	258	15
Income unknown.......	4	†

* Excludes 47 families with either unknown gross charges or unknown net charges.

† Not computed because of small base.

Table A-72. Total Insurance Benefits as a Percentage of Total Gross Charges, for Those Insured Families Who Received Insurance Benefits, by Specified Levels of Gross Charges Incurred and by Income

Income	Number of insured families incurring some gross charges*	Total insurance benefits as % of total gross charges of insured families incurring some gross charges*
All income groups......	546	35
Under $2,000..........	43	52
$2,000–$3,499..........	92	38
3,500– 4,999..........	167	37
5,000– 7,499..........	154	32
7,500 and over........	89	30
Income unknown.......	1	†

* Excludes 38 insured families who received insurance benefits but whose gross or net charges were unknown.

† Not computed because of small base.

Table A-73. Receipt of Voluntary-health-insurance Benefits to Cover Gross Charges for All Personal Health Services

Receipt of insurance benefits to cover gross charges*	Number of families	Per cent of families
Total..........................	*2,809*	*100*
No insurance benefits received†.....	2,207	79
Some insurance benefits received....	602	21
Some part of gross charges covered by insurance benefits..............	*602*	*100*
Under 20% covered................	172	29
20–39% covered..................	170	28
40–59% covered..................	121	20
60–79% covered..................	60	10
80–99% covered.................	44	7
Per cent covered unknown.........	35	6

* Gross charges are here defined as hospital charges, physicians' charges, charges for medicines or medical appliances, charges for other medical services, and dental charges incurred by family members. It does not include travel costs and other costs incidental to illness but only medical services or goods. It does not include the "cost" of free care, but it does include the estimated gross costs for hospital care under a service plan and medical service in the case of services from comprehensive plans. Moreover, these are gross *incurred* charges. That is, they include unpaid bills for services received during the survey year, and they, of course, exclude payments made on bills incurred prior to the survey year. They also exclude the family's medical expense for persons not currently a part of the family unit (except for family members deceased during the survey year), and they exclude premium payments for voluntary health insurance.

Medium per cent of gross charges covered by insurance = 32%. Among those who received insurance benefits, half received amounts which covered 32% or less of gross charges, and half received amounts which covered more than 32%.

† In 224 of these families where no insurance benefits were received, no gross charges had been incurred.

Table A-74. Receipt of Surgical or Medical Insurance Benefits to
Cover Gross Physicians' Charges

Receipt of insurance benefits to cover gross physicians' charges*	Number of families	Per cent of families
Total..............................	*2,809*	*100*
No gross physicians' charges—no insurance benefits received.........	708	25
Some gross physicians' charges—no insurance benefits received........	1,702	61
Some gross physicians' charges—some insurance benefits received........	399	14
Some insurance benefits received to cover gross physicians' charges......	*399*	*100*
Under 20% covered...............	57	14
20–39% covered..................	106	27
40–59% covered..................	78	20
60–79% covered..................	37	9
80% or more covered.............	102	26
Per cent covered unknown..........	19	5

* Gross physicians' charges include all charges by physicians and osteopathic physicians. They exclude charges by chiropractors and other paramedical workers. They also exclude the "cost" of free care. (In about 2 or 3% of all families the only attendance by a physician was free care.)

Median per cent of gross physicians' charges covered by insurance = 54%. In half the families which received surgical or medical insurance benefits, 54% or more of their gross physicians' charges were met by insurance benefits.

Table A-75. Receipt of Hospital-insurance Benefits to
Cover Gross Hospital Charges

Receipt of insurance benefits to cover gross hospital charges*	Number of families	Per cent of families
Total.............................	*2,809*	*100*
No hospital charges................	2,086	74
Hospital charges—no insurance benefits received.....................	281	10
Some hospital insurance benefits received........................	442	16
Some part of gross hospital charges covered by insurance benefits......	*442*	*100*
Under 20% covered................	8	2
20–39% covered...................	27	6
40–59% covered...................	46	10
60–79% covered...................	91	21
80% or more covered.............	263	59
Per cent covered unknown.........	7	2

* Gross hospital charges are the total amount of hospital bills. It includes total room-and-board charges, laboratory fees, drugs, X-rays, and the usual extras, but it does not include special nursing, the anesthetist's fee when anesthesia was administered by an outside anesthetist, or physicians' fees. These gross charges were mainly incurred in connection with inpatient care, but in a few instances they were for emergency outpatient care. Gross hospital charges exclude the "cost" of free care. (About 1 or 2% of families received only free hospital service.)

Median per cent of gross hospital charges covered by hospital insurance = 89%. Among those families who received hospital insurance benefits, 50% had 89% or more of their gross hospital charges covered by hospital insurance benefits, so that their net hospital charges were 11% or less of their total hospital bills.

Table A-76. Percentage Distribution, by Percentage of Hospital Charges Covered by Insurance, for Admissions Where Some Hospital-insurance Benefits Were Received

Per cent of hospital bill covered by hospital-insurance benefits	Hospital admissions,* %		
	All admissions (581†)	Patient covered by one policy (515†)	Patient covered by two policies (66†)
Under 50%...........	7	8	6
50–69%..............	14	13	14
70–89%..............	25	27	13
90–99%..............	13	13	9
100% or more‡........	41	39	58

* Admissions to hospitals classified by the American Hospital Association as general or special long-term, mental and allied, or tuberculosis hospitals are excluded. Only admissions to hospitals classified as general or special short-term by the American Hospital Association and hospitals unlisted but not clearly long-term are included. Only admissions which occurred within the survey year are included. Hospitalizations which began before the survey year but where the patient was still in the hospital at the beginning of the year are excluded. Four admissions where the percentage of the hospital bill covered by insurance is undetermined are excluded.

† Figures equal 100%.

‡ Insurance paid more than the total hospital bill for about 1% of the admissions where the patient was covered by one policy and received benefits. Where the patient was covered by two hospital policies, insurance paid more than the total hospital bill for 36% of the admissions where benefits were received.

Table A-77. Receipt of Surgical or Medical Insurance Benefits
to Cover Gross Surgical Charges

Surgical charges* and benefits	Number of families	Per cent of families
Total..............................	*2,809*	*100*
No gross surgical charges...........	2,423	86
Some gross surgical charges—no insurance benefits received.........	185	7
Some gross surgical charges—some insurance benefits received........	201	7
Some insurance benefits received to cover gross surgical charges.............	*201*	*100*
Under 20% covered...............	7	3
20–39% covered....................	26	13
40–59% covered....................	37	18
60–79% covered....................	33	16
80% or more covered..............	90	45
Per cent covered unknown..........	8	4

* Surgical charges are physicians' charges incurred in connection with surgical procedures, a surgical procedure being defined so as to include the treatment of fractures and dislocations as well as "cutting" procedures. In general, these are the charges for the operations only, but in some instances they include charges for postoperative care.

Median per cent of gross surgical charges covered by insurance = 75%. Half the families who received insurance benefits to cover surgical charges received 75% or more to cover these charges and half received less than 75%.

Table A-78. Receipt of Maternity Benefits to Cover
Gross Obstetrical Charges

Obstetrical charges* and benefits	Number of families	Per cent of families
Total, all families....................	*2,809*	*100*
No gross obstetrical charges.........	2,590	92
Gross obstetrical charges—no insurance benefits received............	147	5
Gross obstetrical charges—insurance benefits received.................	72	3
Some insufance benefits received to cover obstetrical charges................	*72*	*100*
Under 20% covered................	5	7
20–39% covered..................	9	12
40–59% covered..................	21	29
60–79% covered..................	11	15
80% or more covered..............	25	35
Per cent covered unknown..........	1	1

* Gross obstetrical charges include physicians' charges for prenatal care as well as for delivery. Where currently pregnant women had not yet been billed for any part of this care, these charges were treated as not yet incurred. In the case of delivery by Cesarean the charge for the delivery was included under surgical charges.

Median per cent of gross obstetrical charges covered by insurance = 60%. Half the families who received maternity benefits had 60% or more of gross obstetrical charges covered, and half had less than 60% covered.

Table A-79. Mean Percentage of Gross Surgical Charges Covered by Surgical Insurance, and Percentage of Individuals with 80 Per Cent or More of Gross Surgical Charges Covered by Surgical Insurance, by Level of Gross Surgical Charges Incurred

Gross surgical charges	Number of individuals*	Mean per cent of gross surgical charges covered by surgical insurance†	Per cent of individuals with 80% or more of gross surgical charges covered by surgical insurance†
All individuals receiving surgical-insurance benefits............	214	76	52
Individuals having only one operation‡...................	*195*	*76*	*53*
Under $46...................	61	88	75
$ 46–$ 94...................	50	77	46
95– 194...................	57	69	42
195 and over...............	27	64	37
Individuals having two or more operations§.................	*19*	*74*	*42*

* Six individuals whose gross surgical charges or whose surgical insurance benefits were indeterminate are excluded from this table. Note that only individuals who actually received benefits are included here. Thus, those individuals covered by surgical insurance at the time of surgery but who did not receive benefits are excluded.

† The mean percentage of gross surgical charges covered by surgical insurance was computed as follows: Surgical-insurance benefits as a percentage of gross surgical charges was computed for each individual receiving surgical-insurance benefits. These percentages were summed for the specific groupings and divided by the number of individuals in the group. Thus, the experience of every individual was given an equal weight. (The ratio of aggregates could be viewed as the weighted mean of the percentages for individuals, the weights being the size of the gross surgical charges. This view points up the difference in the two statistics.) The mean percentage of gross surgical charges covered by surgical insurance more closely reflects the more frequent experiences with insurance, but it is heavily influenced by extreme experiences—the rare cases where the insurance covered an extremely small proportion of the surgical bill. The percentage of individuals with 80% or more of gross surgical charges covered by surgical insurance is not unduly affected by either the experience of those with large gross surgical charges or by the rare cases with extremely small proportions of the surgical bill covered. But it of course reflects only a small part of the over-all distribution. Eighty per cent was chosen as a dividing point because it is approximately the median percentage covered by surgical insurance.

‡ The statistics for individuals having only one operation can be considered to approximate a distribution by case except that it must be realized that those individuals with particularly expensive operations were likely to have more than one operation. Thus, several unusually expensive operations were excluded from this part of the distribution.

§ Although it is impossible to determine precisely whether insurance benefits were intended to cover one or all of the operations of a given individual, it appears that in the vast majority of these cases both operations were covered. In the few cases where it is apparent that benefits were received for only one of the procedures, it was always the charge for the more expensive procedure which was being indemnified.

Table A-80. Distribution of Gross Charges for All Services, and the Extent to Which Insurance Benefits Covered Gross Charges, for Families Utilizing Insured Services (at Least One Hospitalization and One Surgical Procedure Which Were Covered by Insurance),* by Level of Gross Charges Incurred

Variables	Per cent of charges covered, by level of gross total charges				
	All families with gross total charges (184 families)	$1–$194 (25 families)	$195–$394 (50 families)	$395–$594 (53 families)	$595 and over (56 families)
Mean gross total charges for all services..........................	*$528*	*$141*	*$287*	*$485*	*$957*
Total gross hospital charges covered by insurance...................	76	81	88	74	74
Total gross surgical charges covered by insurance...................	60	71	65	54	61
Total gross hospital and surgical charges covered by insurance.....	70	77	78	65	69
Total gross charges for all services covered by insurance...........	42	40	44	44	41

* Thirty families who utilized insured hospital services are excluded from this table because some part of the charges they incurred or the insurance benefits received were not known. Families are included here where a family member did not receive insurance benefits in connection with a given service even though the member was covered at the time by insurance applicable to that type of service. Insurance benefits were actually received by 92% of the families included in this table. See the second footnote to Table A-81 and the first footnote to Table A-94 for some of the reasons why covered individuals did not receive insurance benefits. Families with covered individuals not receiving benefits are included here to reflect the fact that certain individuals who are considered as insured actually are not eligible for benefits for certain services of the general type for which they are covered.

Table A-81. Hospital Admission Rates, by Age, Sex, and Insurance Status

Age and sex	Number of person-years			Admissions† per 100 person-years		
	All persons*	Insured persons‡	Uninsured persons‡	All persons	Insured persons	Uninsured persons
All persons (male and female), total	8,768	4,764	4,004	12	14	9
Under 6	1,067	586	481	8	9	7
6–17	1,852	1,034	818	8	10	4
18–34	1,958	1,077	881	16	19	13
35–54	2,332	1,424	908	12	14	9
55–64	776	413	363	12	16	7
65 and over§	756	217	539	13	18	11
Age unknown	27	13	14			
Males, total	4,246	2,312	1,934	9	10	6
Under 6	532	284	248	8	10	7
6–17	936	527	409	8	10	4
18–34	908	475	433	6	7	6
35–54	1,136	698	438	10	12	7
55–64	365	203	162	10	14	6
65 and over§	359	119	240	11	13	10
Age unknown	10	6	4			
Females, total	4,522	2,452	2,070	15	17	11
Under 6	535	302	233	8	8	7
6–17	916	507	409	8	10	5
18–34	1,050	602	448	25	28	20
35–54	1,196	726	470	14	17	11
55–64	411	210	201	13	18	7
65 and over§	397	98	291	15	23	13
Age unknown	17	7	10			

* These bases have been adjusted for births and deaths within families to give the population exposed to risk of occurrence.

† An admission is classified here as covered if the patient had hospital insurance in effect at the time of admission. Thus, the admission is classified as covered even if the patient was hospitalized for a condition which was not yet covered under his contract because of a special waiting period for that condition (e.g., deliveries, tonsillectomies, etc.). Also, the admission is classified as covered even though the patient was hospitalized for a condition which was specifically excluded under his contract (e.g., preexisting condition). Admissions to hospitals classified by the American Hospital Association as general or special long-term, mental and allied, or tuberculosis hospitals are excluded. Only admissions to hospitals classified as general or special short-term by the American Hospital Association and hospitals unlisted but not clearly long-term are included. Only admissions which occurred within our survey year are included here. Hospitalizations which began before the survey year but where the patient was still in the hospital at the beginning of the year are excluded.

‡ These bases have been adjusted for persons covered by hospital insurance for only a part of the survey year to give the appropriate insured and noninsured populations exposed to risk of occurrence.

§ The admission rates for persons 65 and over as shown here should be viewed extremely cautiously. Several things cast doubt on them: (1) No other study in the United States has yielded figures this high. See the summary of such studies on p. 285 of vol. 3, *Statistical Appendix*, of the Magnuson report. See also I. S. Falk and Agnes W. Brewster, *Hospitalization and Insurance among Aged Persons*, U.S. Social Security Administration, (Bureau Report 18), Table 34 (following p. 42), for rates by sex groups and insurance status. (2) Other studies indicate that the admission rate among men 65 and over is somewhat higher than the rate for women 65 and over; our sample shows the women with a markedly higher admission rate than men—particularly among the insured.

See the Falk and Brewster paper cited above; Nathan Sinai and Dorothy F. Paton, *Hospitalization of the People of Two Counties: A Study of the Experience in Hillsdale and Branch Counties, Michigan, 1940–1945.* Ann Arbor, Michigan, School of Public Health, University of Michigan, 1949. (Bureau of Public Health Economics. Research Series no. 6); and J. D. Colman, "Age and Sex Variations in Hospital Utilization," *American Journal of Public Health*, 37:1308, 1947. On the other hand: (1) The sampling error in these groups is probably not large enough to account for the differences. This age group was roughly equal in proportion in our total sample to the proportion it represents in the total noninstitutional civilian population, and the sex and age distribution within the 65-and-over group checks against the national population. Thus, there is no reason to suspect any form of sampling bias. (2) All the admissions among the insured women 65 and over were verified and agreed with hospital records, and 75 % of the admissions among the noninsured women were so verified. (3) Further analysis of other characteristics of persons in this age group in our sample may throw light on the differences.

Table A-82. Hospital Admission Rates, Exclusive of Admissions for
Delivery, by Age, Sex, and Insurance Status

Age and sex	Number of person-years			Nondelivery admissions† per 100 person-years		
	All persons*	Insured persons‡	Uninsured persons‡	All persons	Insured persons	Uninsured persons
All persons (male and female), total	8,768	4,764	4,004	10	12	7
Under 6	1,067	586	481	8	9	7
6–17	1,852	1,034	818	7	10	4
18–34	1,958	1,077	881	8	10	7
35–54	2,332	1,424	908	11	13	8
55–64	776	413	363	12	16	6
65 and over	756	217	539	13	18	11
Age unknown	27	13	14			
Males, total	4,246	2,312	1,934	9	10	6
Under 6	532	284	248	8	10	7
6–17	936	527	409	8	10	4
18–34	908	475	433	6	7	6
35–54	1,136	698	438	10	12	7
55–64	365	203	162	10	14	6
65 and over	359	116	240	11	13	10
Age unknown	10	6	4			
Females, total	4,522	2,452	2,070	10	13	8
Under 6	535	302	233	8	8	7
6–17	916	507	409	7	10	4
18–34	1,050	602	448	10	12	8
35–54	1,196	726	470	12	14	8
55–64	411	210	201	13	18	8
65 and over	397	98	299	15	23	13
Age unknown	17	7	10			

* These bases have been adjusted for births and deaths within families to give the population exposed to risk of occurrence.

† An admission is classified here as covered if the patient had hospital insurance in general effect at the time of admission. Thus, the admission is classified as covered even if the patient was hospitalized for a condition which was not yet covered under his contract because of a special waiting period for that condition (e.g., deliveries, tonsillectomies, etc.). Also, the admission is classified as covered even though the patient was hospitalized for a condition which was specifically excluded under his contract (e.g., preexisting condition). Admissions to hospitals classified by the American Hospital Association as general or special long-term, mental and allied, or tuberculosis hospitals are excluded. Only admissions to hospitals classified as general or special short-term by the American Hospital Association and hospitals unlisted but not clearly long-term are included. Only admissions which occurred within our survey year are included here. Hospitalizations which began before the survey year but where the patient was still in the hospital at the beginning of the year are excluded.

‡ These bases have been adjusted for persons covered by hospital insurance for only a part of the survey year to give the appropriate insured and noninsured population exposed to risk of occurrence.

Table A-83. Percentage Distribution of Hospital Admissions, by
Age, Sex, and Insurance Status

Age and sex	Person-years, %			Admissions, %		
	All persons	Insured persons	Uninsured persons	All persons	In-sured persons	Unin-sured persons
All persons (male and female), total* ..	*8,768*	*4,764*	*4,004*	*1,021*	*666*	*355*
Under 6.........	12	12	12	8	8	10
6–17............	21	22	20	14	16	10
18–34...........	22	23	22	31	30	32
35–54...........	27	30	23	28	30	24
55–64...........	9	9	9	9	10	7
65 and over......	9	5	13	10	6	17
Age unknown.....	†	†	†			
Males, total ....*	*4,246*	*2,312*	*1,934*	*365*	*241*	*124*
Under 6.........	13	12	13	12	11	15
6–17............	22	23	21	19	22	14
18–34...........	21	21	22	16	15	19
35–54...........	27	30	23	31	34	26
55–64...........	9	9	8	10	12	8
65 and over......	8	5	12	11	7	19
Age unknown.....	†	†	†			
Females, total ....*	*4,552*	*2,452*	*2,070*	*656*	*425*	*231*
Under 6.........	18	12	11	6	6	7
6–17............	20	21	20	11	12	8
18–34...........	23	25	22	39	40	39
35–54...........	26	30	23	26	28	23
55–64...........	9	9	10	8	9	6
65 and over......	9	4	14	9	5	16
Age unknown.....	†	†	†			

* Figures equal 100%.
† Half, or less than half, of 1%.

Table A-84. Hospital Admission Rates, by Age, Family Income, and Insurance Status

Age and sex	Number of person-years			Admissions† per 100 person-years		
	All persons*	Insured persons‡	Uninsured persons‡	All persons	Insured persons	Uninsured persons
All persons (all ages), total	*8,769*	*4,771*	*3,998*	*12*	*14*	*9*
Under $2,000.........	1,373	321	1,052	12	21	9
$2,000–$3,499........	1,888	840	1,048	12	16	9
3,500– 4,999........	2,368	1,441	927	12	13	9
5,000– 7,499........	1,935	1,359	576	12	13	8
7,500 and over.......	1,161	796	365	11	12	10
All persons under 18, total.	*2,919*	*1,620*	*1,299*	*8*	*10*	*5*
Under $2,000.........	402	94	308	6	7	6
$2,000–$3,499........	662	293	369	10	15	5
3,500– 4,999........	865	530	335	8	9	6
5,000– 7,499........	646	467	179	7	8	3
7,500 and over.......	333	232	101	8	9	7
All persons 18–54, total...	*4,291*	*2,507*	*1,784*	*14*	*16*	*11*
Under $2,000.........	468	117	351	15	24	13
$2,000–$3,499........	896	410	486	15	18	13
3,500– 4,999........	1,208	757	451	15	17	12
5,000– 7,499........	1,051	755	296	14	15	8
7,500 and over.......	648	461	187	12	13	9
All persons 55 and over, total.................	*1,532*	*631*	*901*	*12*	*16*	*10*
Under $2,000.........	499	109	390	13	29	8
$2,000–$3,499........	327	137	190	8	10	7
3,500– 4,999........	290	149	141	10	10	9
5,000– 7,499........	229	132	97	17	20	13
7,500 and over.......	174	101	73	16	16	15

* These bases have been adjusted for births and deaths within families to give the population exposed to risk of occurrence.

† An admission is classified here as covered if the patient had hospital insurance in general effect at the time of admission. Thus, the admission is classified as covered even if the patient was hospitalized for a condition which was not yet covered under his contract because of a special waiting period for that condition (e.g., deliveries, tonsillectomies, etc.). Also, the admission is classified as covered even though the patient was hospitalized for a condition which was specifically excluded under his contract (e.g., preexisting condition). Admissions to hospitals classified by the American Hospital Association as general or special long-term, mental and allied, or tuberculosis hospitals are excluded. Only admissions to hospitals classified as general or special short-term by the American Hospital Association and hospitals unlisted but not clearly long-term are included. Only admissions which occurred within our survey year are included here. Hospitalizations which began before the survey year but where the patient was still in the hospital at the beginning of the year are excluded.

‡ These bases have been adjusted for persons covered by hospital insurance for only a part of the survey year to give the appropriate insured and noninsured population exposed to risk of occurrence.

Table A-85. Hospital Admission Rates, by Sex, Residence, and Insurance Status

Age and sex	Number of person-years			Admissions† per 100 person-years		
	All persons*	Insured persons‡	Uninsured persons‡	All persons	Insured persons	Uninsured persons
All persons (male and female), total.........	*8,769*	*4,771*	*3,998*	*12*	*14*	*9*
Urban, areas of 1 million or more........	2,271	1,381	890	10	12	7
Other urban..........	3,120	1,908	1,212	11	13	10
Rural nonfarm.......	1,783	901	882	14	17	11
Rural farm...........	1,595	581	1,014	12	19	8
Males, total..............	*4,246*	*2,317*	*1,929*	*9*	*10*	*6*
Urban, areas of 1 million or more........	1,080	678	402	8	9	6
Other urban..........	1,480	912	568	9	10	7
Rural nonfarm.......	861	436	425	10	13	7
Rural farm...........	825	291	534	8	11	6
Females, total............	*4,523*	*2,454*	*2,069*	*15*	*17*	*11*
Urban, areas of 1 million or more........	1,191	703	488	12	15	8
Other urban..........	1,640	996	644	14	15	12
Rural nonfarm.......	922	465	457	17	20	14
Rural farm...........	770	290	480	16	27	9

* These bases have been adjusted for births and deaths within families to give the population exposed to risk of occurrence.

† An admission is classified here as covered if the patient had hospital insurance in general effect at the time of admission. Thus the admission is classified as covered even if the patient was hospitalized for a condition which was not yet covered under his contract because of a special waiting period for that condition (e.g., deliveries, tonsillectomies, etc.). Also, the admission is classified as covered even though the patient was hospitalized for a condition which was specifically excluded under his contract (e.g., preexisting condition). Admissions to hospitals classified by the American Hospital Association as general or special long-term, mental and allied, or tuberculosis hospitals are excluded from this tabulation. Only admissions to hospitals classified as general or special short-term by the American Hospital Association and hospitals unlisted by the AHA but not clearly long-term are included here. Only admissions which occurred within our survey year are included here. Hospitalizations which began before the survey year but where the patient was still in the hospital at the beginning of the year are excluded.

‡ These bases have been adjusted for persons covered by hospital insurance for only a part of the survey year to give the appropriate insured and noninsured population exposed to risk of occurrence.

Table A-86. Mean Length of Stay per Admission,* by
Age, Sex, and Insurance Status

Age and sex	Length of stay, days		
	All persons	Persons with hospital insurance	Persons with no hospital insurance
All persons (male and female), total	7.4	7.0	8.3
Under 18	5.3	4.8	6.5
18–54	6.8	6.8	6.7
55 and over	11.9	11.3	12.7
Males, total	8.3	7.1	10.6
Under 18	5.5	4.8	6.9
18–54	8.3	6.5	12.1
55 and over	12.5	12.8	12.1
Females, total	7.0	6.9	7.1
Under 18	5.1	4.7	6.1
18–54	6.3	6.9	5.0
55 and over	11.5	10.2	13.1

* Admissions are classified here on the basis of whether the patient had hospital insurance at the time of admission; *not* on the basis of whether or not benefits were actually received. No insurance benefits at all were received for 12% of those admissions classified here as covered. Admissions to hospitals classified by the American Hospital Association as general or special long-term, mental and allied, or tuberculosis hospitals are excluded. Only admissions to hospitals classified as general or special long-term by the American Hospital Association and hospitals unlisted but not clearly long-term are included here. Only hospital days within the survey year are included. Thus, for admissions occurring before the survey year but extending over into the survey year, only the latter part of the stay is counted. For admissions where the patient had not yet been discharged at the date of interview, only the first part of the stay is counted. The mean number of days is computed as the total number of days divided by the number of admissions within the year.

Table A-87. Percentage Distribution of Length of Stay per Admission,* by Age and Insurance Status

Insurance status and length of stay	Per cent distribution, by age			
	All persons	Under 18	18–54	55 and over
All persons (insured and uninsured), total†	1,033	230	608	195
Under 3	28	49	24	16
3–5	31	22	37	23
6–9	21	17	22	22
10–19	13	8	11	24
20 or more	6	3	4	14
Days unknown	1	‡	1	
Insured persons, total†	670	157	407	106
Under 3	29	52	23	18
3–5	31	22	37	20
6–9	23	15	25	26
10–19	12	8	11	22
20 or more	5	3	3	14
Days unknown	‡		‡	
Uninsured persons, total	363	73	201	89
Under 3	27	42	26	15
3–5	32	22	37	27
6–9	18	22	17	17
10–19	14	7	11	27
20 or more	7	5	5	15
Days unknown	2	1	2	

* An admission is classified here as covered if the patient had hospital insurance in effect at the time of admission. Thus, the admission is classified as covered even if the patient was hospitalized for a condition which was not yet covered under his contract because of a special waiting period for that condition (e.g., deliveries, tonsillectomies, etc.). Also, the admission is classified as covered even though the patient was hospitalized for a condition which was specifically excluded under his contract (e.g., preexisting condition). Admissions to hospitals classified by the American Hospital Association as general or special long-term, mental and allied, or tuberculosis hospitals are excluded. Only admissions to hospitals classified as general or special short-term by the American Hospital Association and hospitals unlisted but not clearly long-term are included. This tabulation includes 12 hospital stays where the patient was actually admitted prior to the survey year but the stay extended into the survey year.

† Figures equal 100%.

‡ Half, or less than half, of 1%.

Table A-88. Mean Hospital Days per 100 Person-years, by Age, Sex, and Insurance Status*

Age and sex	Number of person-years			Mean hospital days per person-year		
	All persons†	Insured persons	Uninsured persons	All persons	Insured persons‡	Uninsured persons
All persons (male and female), total	8,768	4,764	4,004	90	100	70
Under 18	2,919	1,620	1,299	40	50	40
18–54	4,290	2,501	1,789	100	110	80
55 and over	1,532	630	902	150	190	120
Age unknown	27	13	14			
Males, total	4,246	2,312	1,934	70	70	70
Under 18	1,468	811	657	40	50	40
18–54	2,044	1,173	871	70	60	80
55 and over	724	322	402	130	170	100
Age unknown	10	6	4			
Females, total	4,522	2,452	2,070	100	120	80
Under 18	1,451	809	642	40	40	30
18–54	2,246	1,328	918	120	150	80
55 and over	808	308	500	160	200	140
Age unknown	17	7	10			

* An admission is classified here as covered if the patient had hospital insurance in effect at the time of admission. Thus, the admission is classified as covered even if the patient was hospitalized for a condition which was not yet covered under his contract because of a special waiting period for that condition (e.g., deliveries, tonsillectomies, etc.). Also the admission is classified as covered even though the patient was hospitalized for a condition which was specifically excluded under his contract (e.g., preexisting condition). Admissions to hospitals classified by the American Hospital Association as general or special long-term, mental and allied, or tuberculosis hospitals are excluded. Only admissions to hospitals classified as general or special short-term by the American Hospital Association and hospitals unlisted but not clearly long-term are included.

† These bases have been adjusted for births and deaths within families to give the population exposed to risk of occurrence.

‡ These bases have been adjusted for persons covered by hospital insurance for only a part of the survey year to give the appropriate insured and noninsured population exposed to risk of occurrence.

Table A-89. Percentage Distribution of Hospital Days, by
Age, Sex, and Insurance Status

Age and sex	Person-years			Hospital days		
	All persons	Insured persons	Uninsured persons	All persons	Insured persons	Uninsured persons
All persons (male and female), total*....................	8,768	4,746	4,004	7,589	4,659	2,935
Under 6.....................	12	12	12	7	4	10
6-17........................	21	22	20	9	12	6
18-34.......................	22	23	22	25	26	25
35-54.......................	27	30	23	29	33	22
55-64.......................	9	9	9	15	16	13
65 and over................	9	5	13	15	9	25
Age unknown...............	†	†	†			
Males, total...................	4,246	2,312	1,934	3,011	1,707	1,312
Under 6.....................	13	12	13	8	7	11
6-17........................	22	23	21	13	16	8
18-34.......................	21	21	22	21	17	27
35-54.......................	27	30	23	26	27	25
55-64.......................	9	9	8	22	26	16
65 and over................	8	5	12	10	7	15
Age unknown...............	†	†	†			
Females, total.................	4,522	2,452	2,070	4,581	2,952	1,623
Under 6.....................	12	12	11	5	3	9
6-17........................	20	21	20	7	9	4
18-34.......................	23	25	22	29	31	25
35-54.......................	26	30	23	31	37	19
55-64.......................	9	9	10	10	10	10
65 and over................	9	4	14	18	11	33
Age unknown...............	†	†	†			

* Figures equal 100 %.
† Half, or less than half, of 1 %.

Table A-90. Number of Hospital Days per 100 Person-years, by
Family Income and Insurance Status*

Family income	Number of person-years			Number of hospital days per 100 person-years		
	All person-years	Insured person-years	Uninsured person-years	All hospital days	Insured hospital days	Uninsured hospital days
Total*..............	8,769	4,771	3,998	90	100	70
Under $2,000.........	1,373	321	1,052	100	190	80
$2,000–$3,499........	1,888	840	1,048	80	100	60
3,500– 4,999........	2,368	1,441	927	90	110	70
5,000– 7,499........	1,935	1,359	576	70	70	70
7,500 and over.......	1,161	796	365	90	70	110

* Includes 14 insured person-years and 30 uninsured person-years in families
with unknown income.

Table A-91. Distribution of Length of Hospital Stays for Delivery, by Insurance Status at the Time of Confinement

Length of stay, days	Per cent of confinements, by insurance status		
	All confinements (188*)	Insured confinements (114*)	Uninsured confinements (74*)
Under 3.........	15	10	24
3–5.............	57	54	61
6–9.............	26	33	15
10–19..........	2	3	

* Figures equal 100%.

Table A-92. Mean Length of Hospital Stay for Delivery, by Residence
and Insurance Status

Residence	Length of stay, days		
	All confinements	Insured confinements	Uninsured confinements
Total..................	4.7	5.1	4.0
Urban.................	5.0	5.5	4.0
Rural nonfarm...........	4.2	4.7	3.9
Rural farm.............	4.1	4.2	4.1

Table A-93. Percentage Distribution by Daily Room-and-board Rates Charged for Admissions, by Insurance Status

Daily room-and-board rates	Per cent of admissions,* by insurance status				
	All admissions	No hospital insurance	Any hospital insurance	One hospital-insurance plan or policy	Two hospital-insurance plans or policies
Number of known daily room-and-board rates†.........	*805*	*236*	*569*	*510*	*59*
Under $7.................	9	14	7	7	5
$7 but less than $10.........	38	41	37	38	34
$10 but less than $12.......	21	18	23	22	27
$12 but less than $15.......	19	15	21	22	15
$15 but less than $20.......	11	11	11	10	15
$20 or more...............	2	2	2	1	3

* Admissions are classified here on the basis of the type of hospital insurance the patient had at the time of admission; *not* on the basis of whether or not benefits were actually received. No insurance benefits at all were received for 12% of those admissions classified here as covered. Furthermore, benefits were received from both insurers in only half the admissions covered by two plans or policies. Admissions to hospitals classified by the American Hospital Association as general or special long-term, mental and allied, or tuberculosis hospitals are excluded. Only admissions to hospitals classified as general or special short-term by the American Hospital Association or hospitals unlisted but not clearly long-term are included. Only admissions which occurred within our survey year are included here. Hospitalizations which began before the survey year but where the patient was still in the hospital at the beginning of the year are excluded.

† With respect to these totals it should be noted that: (1) If the patient had two types of rooms during a single hospital stay, both rates have been recorded. (2) The daily room-and-board rates were not known for 76 insured admissions and 54 uninsured admissions. (3) For 112 admissions, 39 for insured persons and 73 for uninsured persons, room-and-board rates were not recorded because the patient was a free patient (VA, public assistance, etc.) or because other third parties (mainly workmen's compensation) paid the bill.

Table A-94. Surgical Procedures per 100 Person-years, by Age, Sex, and
Insurance Status*

Age and sex	Person-years			Surgical procedures‡ per 100 person-years		
	All persons†	Surgically insured persons*§	Not surgically insured*§	All persons	Surgically insured persons*	Not surgically insured*
All persons (male and female). total	*8,768*	*3,903*	*4,865*	*7*	*9*	*5*
Under 6		1,067	463	604	4	6	2
6–17		1,852	861	991	6	8	4
18–34		1,958	916	1,042	6	9	4
35–54		2,332	1,167	1,165	8	10	6
55–64		776	321	455	8	9	6
65 and over		756	162	594	6	6	7
Age unknown		27	13	14			
Males, total	*4,246*	*1,912*	*2,334*	*6*	*7*	*4*
Under 6		532	229	303	4	6	3
6–17		936	449	487	7	10	5
18–34		908	403	505	4	5	3
35–54		1,136	580	556	7	9	5
55–64		365	154	211	6	7	5
65 and over		359	91	268	5	4	5
Age unknown		10	6	4			
Females, total	*4,522*	*1,991*	*2,531*	*8*	*10*	*6*
Under 6		535	234	301	4	6	2
6–17		916	412	504	5	7	4
18–34		1,050	513	537	9	12	6
35–54		1,196	587	609	9	11	7
55–64		411	167	244	9	11	7
65 and over		397	71	326	8	8	8
Age unknown		17	7	10			

* A person is here classed as insured if the patient had surgical insurance in general effect at the time the surgical procedure was performed. Thus, the procedure is classified as insured even if *no* insurance benefits were received for reasons like the following: (1) waiting period for particular condition; (2) procedure not covered by particular policy (not classed as surgery by the given policy but generally considered as surgery by other policies or, more frequently, outpatient surgery when only inpatient surgery was indemnifiable under the particular policy); (3) specific exclusion (e.g., preexisting condition); (4) no charge made for the surgery (VA, charity patient, etc.) or charges covered by other third-party payments (workmen's compensation, public welfare, accident insurance, liability insurance, etc.).

† These bases have been adjusted for births and deaths within families to give the population exposed to risk of occurrence.

‡ Surgical procedures are defined as any cutting procedure (including Cesarean but not normal deliveries) or setting of a dislocation or fracture. Two procedures which are often classed as surgical but are not so classed here are circumcision of newborn infants and suturing of wounds.

§ These bases have been adjusted for persons covered by surgical insurance for only a part of the survey year to give the appropriate insured and uninsured population exposed to risk of occurrence. Owing to certain problems of data collection, it was impossible to estimate exposed surgically insured person-years solely from the survey data itself. It was necessary to combine the information obtained in the survey concerning age-sex differentials in part-year coverage of hospital insurance with Health Insurance Council estimates of the differential growth of surgical insurance as compared with hospital insurance in the total population between the end of 1951 and the end of 1953. The combination of the two types of data in estimating the allocation of total person-years into the insured and uninsured categories lessens somewhat the reliability of the insured-uninsured comparisons within specific age-sex groups, but it seems highly unlikely that this procedure has produced fictitious trends in the data. There can be no doubt on these grounds about the basic finding of a higher surgical rate among those covered by surgical insurance than among those not covered. The estimation procedure used does produce differences, of a negligible magnitude, in the estimates of the total surgically insured person-years (also the totals for males and females) between the present table, the rural-urban table, and the tables involving the type of insurer. These differences do not affect the estimates of surgical rates in the significant decimal places.

Table A-95. Surgical Procedures per 100 Person-years, by Sex, Income Groups, and Insurance Status*

Sex and family income	Person-years			Surgical procedures per 100 person-years		
	All persons	Surgically insured persons	Not surgically insured	All persons	Surgically insured persons	Not surgically insured
All persons (male and female), total†	8,769	3,913	4,856	7	9	5
Under $2,000	1,373	236	1,137	6	15	4
$2,000–$3,499	1,888	628	1,260	6	10	4
3,500– 4,999	2,368	1,265	1,103	7	8	6
5,000– 7,499	1,935	1,135	800	8	9	6
7,500 and over	1,161	639	522	7	8	6
Males, total†	*4,246*	*1,918*	*2,328*	*6*	*7*	*4*
Under $2,000	628	100	528	5	14	3
$2,000–$3,499	905	305	600	4	6	4
3,500– 4,999	1,146	608	538	6	7	4
5,000– 7,499	952	558	394	8	9	5
7,500 and over	593	342	251	6	6	6
Females, total†	*4,523*	*1,995*	*2,528*	*8*	*10*	*6*
Under $2,000	745	136	609	6	15	4
$2,000–$3,499	983	323	660	8	14	5
3,500– 4,999	1,222	657	565	8	8	7
5,000– 7,499	983	577	406	8	8	7
7,500 and over	568	297	271	8	9	7

* See footnotes to Table A-94.
† Includes individuals in families with unknown income.

Table A-96. Surgical Procedures per 100 Person-years, by Sex, Residence,
and Insurance Status*

Sex and residence	Person-years			Surgical procedures per 100 person-years		
	All persons	Surgically insured persons	Not surgically insured	All persons	Surgically insured persons	Not surgically insured
All persons (male and female), total.........	*8,769*	*3,906*	*4,863*	*7*	*9*	*5*
Urban, areas of 1 million or more........	2,271	1,050	1,221	6	8	5
Other urban...........	3,120	1,594	1,526	7	9	5
Rural nonfarm........	1,783	767	1,016	6	8	5
Rural farm...........	1,595	495	1,100	7	12	4
Males, total..............	*4,246*	*1,916*	*2,330*	*6*	*7*	*4*
Urban, areas of 1 million or more........	1,080	517	563	6	7	5
Other urban...........	1,480	777	703	6	8	4
Rural nonfarm........	861	373	488	4	6	3
Rural farm...........	825	249	576	6	9	5
Females, total.............	*4,523*	*1,990*	*2,533*	*8*	*10*	*6*
Urban, areas of 1 million or more........	1,191	533	658	7	9	5
Other urban...........	1,640	817	823	8	9	6
Rural nonfarm........	922	394	528	9	9	8
Rural farm...........	770	246	524	7	14	4

* See footnotes to Table A-94.

Table A-97. Estimated Percentage Who Did Not See a Physician during the
Survey Year as Outpatients, and Estimated Percentage Who Had 15
or More Outpatient Physicians' Calls, for Individuals,
by Sex, Age, and Insurance Status

Age, sex, and insurance status	Number of individuals	Estimated per cent with no outpatient physicians' calls*	Estimated per cent with 15 or more outpatient physicians' calls†
All persons (male and female), all ages‡......	*8,898*	*40*	*7*
Under 6..............	1,177	28	3
6–17.................	1,852	48	2
18–34...............	1,959	37	6
35–54...............	2,336	41	8
55–64...............	780	42	12
65 and over..........	767	35	13
Males, all ages‡..........	*4,311*	*45*	*4*
Under 6..............	586	30	3
6–17.................	936	52	2
18–34...............	908	50	3
35–54...............	1,138	47	5
55–64...............	• 367	44	9
65 and over..........	366	40	9
Female, all ages‡..........	*4,587*	*35*	*9*
Under 6..............	591	27	3
6–17.................	916	46	3
18–34...............	1,051	28	9
35–54...............	1,198	35	11
55–64...............	413	41	15
65 and over..........	401	32	17
All insured§..............	*5,054*	*36*	*7*
Males..............	2,440	40	5
Females..............	2,614	31	9
All uninsured§............	*3,844*	*45*	*6*
Males..............	1,871	51	4
Females..............	1,973	39	8

*Information was collected concerning physicians' calls during the entire
survey year in connection with "major illnesses" and for only the last 6 months
of the year in connection with "minor illnesses." "Major" and "minor" illnesses
were *arbitrarily* distinguished in terms of the *utilization* of medical care, solely as
a data-collecting device. The distinction is in no way meant to reflect the relative
seriousness of the illnesses in medical terms, since an illness classified as "minor"
may have been far more disabling medically (even in terms of the amount of care
which would have been desirable) than an illness classified as "major." The utilization and cost criteria were not intended to reflect anything about the nature of
the illness. The percentages were estimated by making two assumptions. The
assumptions are that, among those individuals who did not see a physician for a
"major illness" during the survey year, (1) the same proportion of individuals

Table A-97 (Continued)

saw a physician during the first half of the survey year as during the second half; and (2) those individuals who saw a physician for a "minor illness" during the second half of the survey year were twice as likely to have seen a physician for a "minor illness" during the first half of the survey year than were those individuals who did not see a physician during the second half.

† These percentages were estimated by assuming that one-fourth of those individuals who had a total of 10–14 physicians' calls for "major illnesses" and for "minor illnesses" during the second half-year had enough "minor illness" physicians' calls during the first half of the survey year to shift them into the 15-or-more-calls category. It should be noted that the vast bulk of those individuals here classified as having had 15 or more calls actually had that many calls in connection with "major illnesses" alone. The increment added on the assumption that one-fourth of the 10–14-call group had sufficient unreported calls to shift them into the higher group was in no instance greater than 2% and was usually only 1%.

‡ Includes individuals whose age was unknown.

§ Insured persons are persons with hospital insurance at the end of the survey year.

Table A-98. Percentage of Persons Receiving Dental Services, by Age and Sex

Age	Number			Per cent consulting a dentist		
	All persons	Males	Females	All persons	Males	Females
Total†	8,846	4,284	4,562	34	31	36
Under 6	1,171	584	587	10	9	10
6–17	1,851	936	915	44	42	47
18–34	1,957	907	1,050	44	40	48
35–54	2,327	1,133	1,194	39	35	42
55–64	773	363	410	25	24	26
65 and over	740	351	389	13	13	12
Age unknown	27	10	17	*	*	*

* Percentage not computed for groups of less than 50.
† Includes only persons alive at the end of the survey year.

Table A-99. Percentage of Persons Consulting Dentists, by Family Income

Family income	Number of persons	Per cent of persons consulting a dentist
Total†..................	8,846	34
Under $2,000............	1,378	17
$2,000-$3,499............	1,912	23
3,500- 4,999............	2,397	33
5,000- 7,499............	1,950	44
7,500 and over..........	1,166	56
Income unknown.........	43	*

* Percentage not computed for groups of less than 50 persons.
† Includes only persons alive at the end of the survey year.

Table A-100. Percentage of Persons Consulting Dentists, by Hospital-insurance Status and Income

Income	Number of persons			Per cent of persons consulting dentists		
	All persons	Persons with hospital insurance*	Persons with no hospital insurance	All persons	Persons with hospital insurance*	Persons with no hospital insurance
Total†..........	8,846	5,042	3,804	34	40	26
Under $2,000.....	1,378	356	1,022	17	18	16
$2,000–$3,499.....	1,912	925	987	23	25	22
3,500– 4,999.....	2,397	1,524	873	33	35	28
5,000– 7,499.....	1,950	1,392	558	44	47	37
7,500 or more....	1,166	832	334	56	59	47

* Insured persons are those with hospital insurance at the end of the survey year.
† Includes persons with unknown income, who are not shown separately in table. Only persons alive at the end of the survey year are included.

Table A-101. Percentage of Persons Receiving Any Kind of Optical Services, by Age and Sex

Age	Number			Per cent receiving optical services		
	All persons	Males	Females	All persons	Males	Females
Total†	8,846	4,284	4,562	14	13	16
Under 6	1,171	584	587	1	1	1
6–17	1,851	936	915	11	10	12
18–34	1,957	907	1,050	14	12	16
35–54	2,327	1,133	1,194	20	17	23
55–64	773	363	410	23	21	24
65 and over	740	351	389	18	15	21
Age unknown	27	10	17	*	*	*

* Percentage not computed for groups of less than 50.
† Includes only persons alive at the end of the survey year.

Table A-102. Percentage Distribution of Admissions, by Percentage of Hospital Bill Covered by Insurance, for Admissions Where the Patient Was Covered by Only One Policy and Where Some Hospital-insurance Benefits Were Received, by Type of Insurance Carrier

Per cent of hospital bill covered by hospital-insurance benefits	Per cent distribution of admissions* where patient received benefits						
	From Blue Cross			From private carrier			Independent (52†)
	All (241†)	Group (177†)	Non-group (64†)	All (222†)	Group (133†)	Non-group (89†)	
Under 50%.........	7	6	11	8	5	12	8
50–69%............	13	14	9	16	6	32	5
70–89%............	26	25	30	29	30	26	20
90–99%............	15	15	14	14	19	8	5
100% or more‡.....	39	40	36	33	40	22	62

* Admissions to hospitals classified by the American Hospital Association as general or special long-term, mental and allied, or tuberculosis hospitals are excluded. Only admissions to hospitals classified as general or short-term by the American Hospital Association and hospitals unlisted but not clearly long-term are included. Four admissions where the percentage of the hospital bill covered is undetermined are excluded.

† Figures equal 100%.

‡ Insurance paid more than the total hospital bill for about 1% of the admissions where the patient was covered by one policy and received benefits.

Table A-103. Percentage Distribution of Admissions, by Percentage of Hospital Bill Covered by Insurance for Admissions Where Patient Was Covered by One Policy and Where Some Hospital-insurance Benefits Were Received, by Type of Enrollment

Per cent of hospital bill covered by hospital-insurance benefits	Per cent distribution of admissions* where patients received benefits	
	From group insurance (358†)	From nongroup insurance (157†)
Under 50%..................	6	12
50–69%....................	10	22
70–89%....................	26	27
90–99%....................	15	10
100% or more‡..............	43	29

* Admissions to hospitals classified by the American Hospital Association as general or special long-term, mental and allied, or tuberculosis hospitals are excluded. Only admissions to hospitals classified as general or short-term by the American Hospital Association and hospitals unlisted but not clearly long-term are included. Only admissions which occurred within the survey year are included. Hospitalizations which began before the survey year, but where the patient was still in the hospital at the beginning of the year are excluded. Four admissions where the percentage of the hospital bill covered is undetermined are excluded.

† Figures equal 100%.

‡ Insurance paid more than the total hospital bill for about 1% of the admissions where the patient was covered by one policy and received benefits.

Table A-104. Percentage Distribution of Hospital Admissions Where the Patient
Was Covered by Only One Policy, by Type of Accommodiation and
Hospital-insurance Coverage

Type of hospital accommodations†	Per cent of admissions*				
	By type of enrollment		By type of insurer		
	Group (407)	Nongroup (186)	Blue Cross (269)	Private (264)	Independent (60)
Private room............	19	29	24	25	5
Semiprivate room........	50	38	50	41	47
Ward..................	29	33	24	33	45
Indeterminate..........	2	...	2	1	3

* Admissions are classified here on the basis of the type of hospital insurance the patient had at the time of admission; not on the basis of whether or not benefits were actually received. No insurance benefits at all were received for 12% of those admissions classified here as covered. Furthermore, benefits were received from both insurers in only half the admissions covered by two plans or policies. Admissions to hospitals classified by the American Hospital Association as general or special long-term, mental and allied, or tuberculosis hospitals are excluded. Only hospitals unlisted but not clearly long-term are included. Only admissions which occurred within our survey year are included. Hospitalizations which began before the survey year but where the patient was still in the hospital at the beginning of the year are excluded.

† In 3% of these admissions the patient occupied two different types of accommodations during a single period of hospitalization. In those instances, the admission was classified according to the best accommodations occupied. Thus, "private and semiprivate," and "private and ward," were classified as "private." "Semiprivate and ward" were classified as "semiprivate."

Table A-105. Percentage Distribution of Daily Room-and-board Rates Charged for Admissions Where the Patient Was Covered by Only One Policy by Type of Enrollment and Insurance

Daily room-and-board rate	Per cent of admissions*				
	By type of enrollment		By type of insurer		
	Group insurance (350†)	Nongroup insurance (160†)	Blue Cross (246†)	Private (213†)	Independent (51†)
Under $7.............	7	7	5	9	6
$7 but less than $10......	35	43	28	49	33
$10 but less than $12.....	25	16	24	19	29
$12 but less than $15.....	21	24	26	17	22
$15 but less than $20.....	11	9	15	6	8
$20 or more............	1	1	2	...	2

* Admissions are classified here on the basis of the type of hospital insurance the patient had at the time of admission; *not* on the basis of whether or not benefits were actually received. No insurance benefits at all were received for 12% of those admissions classified here as covered. Furthermore, benefits were received from both insurers in only half the admissions covered by two plans or policies. Admissions to hospitals classified by the American Hospital Association as general or special long-term, mental and allied, or tuberculosis hospitals are excluded. Only admissions to hospitals classified as general or special short-term by the American Hospital Association and hospitals unlisted but not clearly long-term are included. Only admissions which occurred within our survey year are included. Hospitalizations which began before the survey year but where the patient was still in the hospital at the beginning of the year are excluded.

† With respect to these totals, it should be noted that: (1) If the patient had two types of rooms during a single hospital stay, both rates have been recorded. (2) The daily room-and-board rates were not known for 76 insured admissions. (3) For 39 admissions, room-and-board rates were not recorded because the patient was a free patient (VA, public assistance, etc.) or because other third parties (mainly workmen's compensation) paid the bill.

Table A-106. Mean Gross Surgical Charges per Individual with Some Gross Surgical Charges, by Type of Insurer under Which the Individual Was Covered at the Time of Surgery

Type of insurer	Number of individuals	Mean gross surgical charges per individual
All individuals with some gross surgical charges who were covered by surgical insurance at the time of surgery*.....	268	$96
Individuals covered by one policy at the time of surgery...................	*248*	*$97*
Blue Shield†......................	98	$94
Private, group....................	82	95
Private, nongroup.................	48	107
Independent......................	20	90
Individuals covered by more than one policy at the time of surgery..........	*20*	*89*

* Includes individuals who did not receive surgical benefits but who were covered by surgical insurance at the time of their surgery.

† Includes Blue Cross surgical coverage in states where Blue Cross offers surgical insurance, e.g., California, Washington, and Oregon.

Table A-107. Admission Rates for Persons with Different Types of
Hospital Insurance

Type of hospital insurance	Person-years*	Admissions† per 100 person-years
All persons with hospital insurance..........	4,764	14
Persons with only one hospital plan or policy...	*4,310*	*14*
Blue Cross only........................	1,991	14
Private insurance only..................	1,893	14
Independent only.......................	426	14
One group plan only....................	3,074	13
One nongroup plan only.................	1,236	15
Persons with two or more hospital plans or policies.................................	*454*	*16*

* An admission is classified here as covered if the patient had hospital insurance in general effect at the time of admission. Thus, the admission is classified as covered even if the patient was hospitalized for a condition which was not yet covered under his contract because of a special waiting period for that condition (e.g., deliveries, tonsillectomies, etc.). Also, the admission is classified as covered even though the patient was hospitalized for a condition which was specifically excluded under his contract (e.g., preexisting condition). Admissions to hospitals classified by the American Hospital Association as general or special long-term, mental and allied, or tuberculosis hospitals are excluded. Only admissions to hospitals classified as general or special short-term by the American Hospital Association and hospitals unlisted but not clearly long-term are included. Only admissions which occurred within our survey year are included. Hospitalizations which began before the survey year but where the patient was still in the hospital at the beginning of the year are excluded.

† These bases have been adjusted for persons covered by each type of insurance for only a part of the year to give the appropriate populations exposed to risk of occurrence.

Table A-108. Mean Percentage of Gross Surgical Charges Covered by Surgical
Insurance, and Percentage of Individuals with 80 Per Cent or More of
Gross Surgical Charges Covered by Surgical Insurance, by
Type of Insurer from Which Benefits Were Received

Type of insurer from which benefits were received	Number of individuals*		Mean per cent of gross surgical charges covered by surgical insurance*		Per cent of individuals with 80% or more of gross surgical charges covered by surgical insurance*	
All individuals receiving surgical insurance benefits..............	214		76		52	
Individuals receiving benefits from						
only one type of insurer........	*207*		*76*		*51*	
Blue Shield†..................		83		78		54
Private, group................		70		72		43
Private, nongroup.............		34		66		38
Independent..................		20		94		85
Individuals receiving benefits from						
more than one type of insurer.....	*7*		‡		‡	

* See the first two footnotes to Table A-79.
† Includes Blue Cross surgical coverage in states where Blue Cross offers surgical insurance, e.g., California, Washington, and Oregon.
‡ Not computed because of small base.

Methodology

JACOB J. FELDMAN

National Opinion Research Center

Methodology

Certain general statements about the scope, methods, and limitations of this study are presented for the guidance of the reader in evaluating and making use of the concrete findings. These statements were designed mainly for the general reader rather than for the few persons who will be greatly interested in methods and procedures in a technical sense.[1]

SOURCES OF THE DATA

The study reported here was focused on the role of voluntary health insurance in ameliorating the economic problems which families face in meeting the charges they incur for medical care. To discover the full range of problems these charges pose for the affected individuals and families, it was necessary to examine them within the variable contexts of family circumstances. The kinds and amounts of medical care needed during any given interval of time vary widely from family to family. The affected families also vary widely in their incomes and in the other financial resources they have available to meet the charges involved in securing needed care. The severity of the economic problem precipitated by illness is, therefore, variable; it is dependent on the magnitude of the expenses medical care entails in relation to the financial resources of the family. Similarly, the efficacy of prepaid medical insurance in ameliorating these problems depends on the distribution of insurance coverage among families in relation to the distribution of illnesses, medical expenses, incomes, and other relevant family characteristics.

Relationships of the kind just indicated cannot be ascertained in sufficiently detailed and comprehensive terms from information cur-

[1] Because of the length and complexity of the interview questionnaire, it is not practical to include it in this report. Anyone desiring further information concerning any of the points covered in this appendix or a copy of the questionnaire should write to Jacob J. Feldman, National Opinion Research Center, University of Chicago, 5711 S. Woodlawn Avenue, Chicago 37, Illinois.

rently available from the *suppliers* of medical goods and services, because information from these sources is, in most cases, irrevocably divorced from individual family contexts. To procure data that could be reliably distributed among families, it was necessary to go directly to the *consumers* of medical goods and services of all kinds. Data were collected through detailed personal interviews with one or more responsible adult members of each family in a random national sample of families.

Only Direct Personal Expenditures Examined

When interest centers, as it did in this study, on the extent to which paying for health care is a problem for insured and uninsured families which differ in their age structure, size, financial resources, and other important characteristics, accurate information about *direct personal expenditures*, distributed among individual families, is sufficient. Such information, however, does not include expenditures for medical goods and services made by business firms, eleemosynary agencies, and governmental and other public bodies. It therefore requires supplementation from other sources if it is to be used in deriving estimates of aggregate expenditures for medical care for the country as a whole. In a good many instances, the additions required are relatively small, since, in the United States, direct personal expenditures for health care bulk much larger than indirect expenditures from public and other sources; by far the larger proportion of health care is paid for on a fee-for-service basis.[2] Nonetheless, expenditures from nonfamily sources have to be added to the expenditures from family sources to derive adequate measures of the total amount spent for any particular kind of health care during the year covered by this study.

Institutional Population Not Included

There is a second reason why aggregate estimates of medical care received, expenses attendant on such care, and insurance coverage would be somewhat too low if based only on the data developed in this study. Certain types of consumers of medical goods and services

[2] It perhaps should be noted in this connection that expenditures from nonfamily sources do, in some part, devolve ultimately on the consuming families in the form of taxes, contributions, and concealed payments, and represent family costs, even though they are borne indirectly. But such indirect costs are less problematical for families because they can be anticipated in advance, and each family's assessment is generally roughly proportionate to its income.

were not included in the sample of families from whom our data were collected. Our sample was drawn to represent only the noninstitutionalized population of the continental United States and hence does not include:

1. Residents on military reservations.
2. Residents in medical, mental, penal, religious, or other institutions who were not considered to be current members of noninstitutional households in July, 1953.
3. Transients—persons with no permanent or usual place of residence.

On the basis of the 1950 census it is estimated that about 97 per cent of the population residing in the continental United States in July, 1953, was noninstitutional in character. Hence the proportion of the total population excluded from our study is relatively small. Further, since the primary concern in this study is the evaluation of the efficacy of voluntary prepayment, the exclusion of this institutional population, which is generally outside the health-insurance market, seems particularly appropriate. The exclusion of this group also would have but slight effect on our estimates of expenses borne directly by consumers, since the care of most of this institutional population is provided in considerable part by public funds. Nevertheless, this exclusion does have a marked influence on the over-all estimates of the utilization of hospital and other medical facilities, because in general people residing in institutions are disproportionately great users of medical care. Thus, if one wished to assess the demand placed on the nation's total medical facilities, the present estimates would have to be adjusted for the excluded institutional population. We have not attempted any such adjustments, because this study is focused on the economic problems of the consumers of medical care and not on problems concerning the facilities through which that care is provided.

Data Pertain to One Year Only

Note should be taken here, also, of a third general limitation on the data collected in the course of this study. The data pertained to the period between July 1, 1952, and June 30, 1953. Aggregate estimates derived from them may not accurately reflect experience in other years; it is conceivable that the general level of expenditures in the survey year was somewhat unusual or that, in any case, expenditures during that year are not likely to accurately reflect experience in subsequent years. However, as indications of the way in which medical care and its costs are distributed among families differing in age structure, income, insurance coverage, and other relevant characteristics, they are likely to have a much more stable value. It is unlikely that the general shapes of the distributions and the general direction and magnitude of differences among subgroups in the population have changed markedly since 1952–1953 or that they will change markedly in the next few years.

SIZE AND CHARACTER OF THE SAMPLE

The estimates appearing in this report are based on data concerning 8,898 individuals in 2,809 families. This sample of families was randomly selected from the approximately 50 million families, having a total membership of approximately 155 million individuals, comprising the noninstitutional population of continental United States at the time of the survey. Data were collected through interviews with one or more responsible adult members of each of these families during the early summer of 1953.

The sample used was of the "area-probability" type; it resembled in general design the sample used by the United States Bureau of the Census for the Current Population Survey (Monthly Report on the Labor Force).[3]

Sampling procedures were designed to give every family in the noninstitutional population an equal chance of being selected. Multistage sampling was employed: (1) a sample of relatively large, geographically defined, administrative units (standard metropolitan areas or counties) was drawn by random methods, after stratification; (2) within these primary sampling units, secondary sampling units (towns, villages, and other "localities") were defined and subsampled in a corresponding manner; (3) within these secondary sampling units, in turn, tertiary sampling units (census tracts, etc.) were defined and subsampled; this process was continued through the selection of the ultimate "units of observation" (families).

More specifically, all standard metropolitan areas as defined by the 1950 Census of Population and all individual counties outside the standard metropolitan areas (approximately 3,000 metropolitan areas

---

[3] For a statement of the principles and methods employed in drawing an area-probability sample, see M. H. Hansen, W. N. Hurwitz, and W. G. Madow, *Sample Survey Methods and Theory*, New York, John Wiley & Sons, Inc., 1953.

and counties all together) were grouped into 91 strata according to certain relevant criteria (geographic region, size of largest community in unit, median family income, economic character, availability of certain medical facilities, and others), and one of these primary sampling units was selected from each stratum by a random process, with every one of the approximately 3,000 units having a probability of being selected proportionate to its estimated 1953 population. As a result of this method of selection, the 91 primary sampling units contained approximately 40 per cent of the total population of the country. Corresponding methods of stratification and random selection with probability proportionate to size were employed in selecting localities (331 in all) within the 91 primary sampling units, and in selecting small segments within localities. The final step in sampling involved preparing ordered lists of all the dwelling units in each of the approximately 840 small sample segments and then selecting, again by random methods, the particular dwelling units in which data were to be collected.

Interviewers were instructed to collect data pertaining to every individual member of every family residing in each sample dwelling unit, a family being defined as "one person, or a group of persons living together and related to each other by blood, marriage, or adoption." All such related people were treated as one family unit, except when there were two related married couples living in the same dwelling unit, in which case each married couple and its unmarried children were treated as a separate family. Each person living in the dwelling unit who was unrelated to anyone else in the unit (e.g., lodger or servant) was also treated as a separate family.

Accuracy of Estimates Based on Sampling

It has been well established by mathematical proof and by practical experience that reasonably accurate estimates for an entire population can be derived from a sample of the character and size used in this study, provided that the work of collecting data from the sample is competently done.[4] But no estimate should be assumed to be absolutely accurate. There is always a possibility that a given estimate may be

[4] The reader, should he have any doubts about the plausibility of this statement, is urged to consult the extensive literature on sample surveys, where he will find this point adequately discussed. See, for instance, Hansen, Hurwitz, and Madow, *op. cit.*

somewhat in error, first because it is based on data collected from a sample rather than from every member of a population, and also because the group of people actually interviewed never exactly reproduces the sample as designed.

There are, of course, other sources of possible error than the two just mentioned. For instance, respondents may inaccurately recall or report the information asked for, or the interviewer may ask a question improperly or may inaccurately record the information given him; errors may be made, also, in classifying and tabulating the information reported by the interviewers. But these factors may affect the results of a complete census as well as of a sampling study. In fact, the data collected from a sample, notwithstanding the allowances for possible error that have to be made just because of sampling, may more accurately describe a total population than would a complete census of that population, because it is generally more feasible to control the nonsampling sources of error in a small-scale survey than in a very large one. These sources will be dealt with in subsequent sections of this appendix; in the present section attention is limited to sources of possible error peculiar to sampling surveys.

Whenever statistics for a population are estimated from data collected from a sample of that population, it is likely that the estimates will be somewhat higher or lower than the figures which would have been obtained had a census of the entire population been made. Assuming that just as accurate data would be collected for each family in the complete census as in the sampling survey, we can consider any discrepancy between an estimate made from the sample survey and the results of the complete census an *estimating error due to sampling*. Estimating errors due to sampling may result from any one of three elements involved in the design and execution of a sample survey.

First, owing to the operation of chance alone, the frequency with which any characteristic appears in a randomly selected sample may differ from its frequency in the population sampled. An error that is attributable to this element of chance in the selection of cases to be included in the sample is here referred to as a *sampling deviation*. For any estimate derived from a particular sample survey, the magnitude of the sampling deviation is usually unknown, since no corresponding figure based on a complete census is available. However, sampling theory provides means of computing the probability that the deviation, if any, will fall within certain specifiable limits.

Second, it is never feasible in an interview survey to obtain information from every family or individual selected for the sample. If the distribution of a characteristic among families or individuals where interviews cannot be obtained differs somewhat from its distribution among those from whom information is obtained, then for this characteristic there is likely to be a discrepancy between the estimate derived from the sample survey and the estimate that would have been obtained from a complete census. Such a discrepancy is called a *nonresponse error.*

Third, departures from the sample design may arise in the field execution of the survey; mistakes may be made in identifying and locating sample families or individuals. Any discrepancies in the estimates that result from this fact are called *errors of execution.*

Sampling Deviations

It is possible to calculate the probability that a sampling deviation of more than a specified size will occur by chance in making a particular estimate. We can thus state, for example, that the chances are roughly 2 to 1 that the sampling deviation of a given estimate would be no larger than some specified amount. The margin of error to which these 2-to-1 odds can be attached is called the *standard error of the estimate.*[5] The odds are about 20 to 1 that a sampling deviation will be no greater than twice the standard error and 100 to 1 that it will be no greater than 2.6 standard errors.

Table B-1 shows in Column 3 the standard errors of a number of estimates made in this report. It can be seen there, for instance, that the odds are about 20 to 1 that an estimate, from a sample like the present one, of the percentage of the population covered by hospital insurance would *not* deviate more than three percentage points from the figure obtained in a complete census, if there were no nonresponse

[5] The odds that a sampling deviation will be no greater than one standard error are more exactly 2.15 to 1. The entire discussion here is based on the assumption that the variables under consideration are so distributed and that the sample design (including the size) is such that sampling deviations for each variable will be normally distributed. The validity of this assumption can be judged by the reader from the distributional data presented in this report and from the more detailed account of the sampling design. We are of the opinion that this assumption is close enough to being correct for the present purposes.

A further assumption involved is that we can accurately estimate the variance of the distributions of sampling deviations, even if they are felt to be normal distributions.

Table B-1. Sampling Errors of Selected Ratios and Differences between Ratios

Characteristic	Number of units	Average, per cent, or difference	Estimated standard errors of estimates		Ratio of estimated S.E.'s
			For design used	For simple random sampling	
	(1)	(2)	(3)	(4)	(5)
Gross costs per individual:					
With no hospital insurance...	3,836	$ 54.45	3.24	2.39	1.36
With hospital insurance......	5,038	74.08	2.45	2.29	1.07
All individuals..............	8,874	65.59	1.99	1.69	1.18
Difference.................	....	19.63	4.18	3.46	1.21
Gross physicians' costs per individual:					
55 years old or over.........	1,537	$ 35.00	2.34	2.21	1.06
Under 55 years (or age unknown)..................	7,344	22.84	1.01	0.89	1.13
All individuals..............	8,881	24.94	0.90	0.84	1.07
Difference.................	....	12.16	2.61	2.39	1.09
Per cent hospitalized:					
With no hospital insurance...	3,844	6.0	0.50	0.38	1.32
With hospital insurance......	5,054	9.2	0.49	0.41	1.20
All individuals..............	8,898	7.9	0.37	0.29	1.28
Difference.................	....	3.2	0.69	0.56	1.23
Per cent of individuals with no hospital insurance:					
"Employees" or spouse or children.................	5,711	29.7	1.60	0.60	2.67
Others....................	3,135	67.2	1.77	0.84	2.11
All uninsured individuals....	8,846	43.0	1.48	0.53	2.79
Difference.................	....	37.5	2.12	1.03	2.06
Per cent having surgery:					
With no surgical insurance...	4,584	3.9	0.36	0.29	1.24
With surgical insurance......	4,314	6.9	0.37	0.38	0.97
All individuals..............	8,898	5.4	0.27	0.24	1.26
Difference.................	....	3.0	0.51	0.48	1.06
Uninsured hospital admissions per 100 uninsured person-years:					
Persons 55 years old and over	910	9.5	1.22	0.97	1.26
Persons under 55 years (or age unknown)............	3,123	8.6	0.69	0.50	1.38
All uninsured person-years...	4,033	8.8	0.66	0.45	1.47
Difference.................	....	0.9	1.23	1.09	1.13

Table B-1 (Continued)

Characteristic	Number of units	Average, per cent, or difference	Estimated standard errors of estimates		Ratio of estimated S.E.'s
			For design used	For simple random sampling	
	(1)	(2)	(3)	(4)	(5)
Hospital admissions per 100 person-years for persons 55 years old or over:					
Uninsured persons..........	910	9.5	1.22	0.97	1.26
Insured persons.............	606	17.1	2.13	1.52	1.40
All persons 55 years old or over....................	1,516	12.5	1.15	0.84	1.37
Difference.................	....	7.6	2.46	1.81	1.36
Insured hospital admissions per insured 100 person-years:					
Persons 55 years old and over .	606	17.2	2.13	1.53	1.39
Persons under 55 years (or age unknown)............	4,086	13.8	0.67	0.54	1.24
All insured person-years.....	4,692	14.2	0.71	0.51	1.39
Difference.................	....	3.4	2.18	1.63	1.34
Hospital admissions per 100 person-years for persons under 55 years (or age unknown):					
Uninsured persons..........	3,123	8.6	0.69	0.50	1.38
Insured persons	4,086	13.8	0.67	0.54	1.24
All persons under 55 years...	7,209	11.5	0.49	0.38	1.29
Difference.................	....	5.2	0.93	0.74	1.26
Hospital days per 100 person-years for persons 55 years old or over:					
Uninsured persons..........	910	120.1	22.81	20.70	1.00
Insured persons.............	606	193.4	31.40	30.43	1.03
All persons 55 and over......	1,516	149.4	18.31	17.40	1.05
Difference.................	....	73.3	39.88	36.80	1.08
Hospital days per 100 person-years for persons under 55 years (or age unknown):					
Uninsured persons..........	3,123	57.4	7.63	6.40	1.19
Insured persons.............	4,086	85.0	9.84	9.60	1.03
All persons under 55 years...	7,209	73.0	6.68	6.10	1.10
Difference.................	....	27.6	11.96	11.50	1.04

Table B-1 (Continued)

| Characteristic | Number of units | Average, per cent, or difference | Estimated standard errors of estimates | | Ratio of estimated S.E.'s |
| | | | For design used | For simple random sampling | |
	(1)	(2)	(3)	(4)	(5)
Hospital days per admission for uninsured admissions:					
Persons 55 years old or over..	86	12.7	1.75	1.76	0.99
Persons under 55 years......	263	6.8	0.64	0.64	1.00
All uninsured admissions.....	349	8.3	0.69	0.66	1.05
Difference..................	....	5.9	1.84	1.87	0.98
Hospital days per insured admission:					
Persons 55 years old or over..	104	11.3	1.52	1.45	1.05
Persons under 55 years......	560	6.2	0.66	0.66	1.00
All persons................	664	7.0	0.63	0.60	1.05
Difference..................	....	5.1	1.62	1.59	1.02
Per cent of families with incomes less than $2,000 having net costs of $45 or less:					
Uninsured families.........	395	50.9	2.75	2.51	1.10
Insured families...........	178	38.2	4.01	3.64	1.10
All families (less than $2,000 income).................	573	46.9	2.46	2.08	1.18
Difference..................	....	12.7	4.59	4.43	1.04
Per cent of families with incomes $2,000–$3,499 having net costs of $45 or less:					
Uninsured families.........	266	45.1	3.21	3.05	1.05
Insured families...........	340	32.9	2.92	2.55	1.15
All families (income $2,000–$3,499).................	606	38.3	1.86	1.97	0.94
Difference..................	....	12.2	4.92	3.98	1.24
Per cent of families having net costs of $45 or less:					
Uninsured families.........	1,019	42.6	1.89	1.55	1.22
Insured families...........	1,761	24.6	1.14	1.03	1.11
All families................	2,780	31.2	1.13	0.88	1.28
Difference..................	....	18.0	2.13	1.86	1.15

Table B-1 (Continued)

Characteristic	Number of units	Average, per cent, or difference	Estimated standard errors of estimates For design used	Estimated standard errors of estimates For simple random sampling	Ratio of estimated S.E.'s
	(1)	(2)	(3)	(4)	(5)
Per cent of uninsured families having net costs of $45 or less:					
Family income under $2,000..	395	50.9	2.75	2.51	1.10
Family income $2,000–$3,499.	266	45.1	3.21	3.05	1.05
All families (income less than $3,500).................	661	48.6	2.31	1.94	1.19
Difference..................	......	5.8	3.75	3.95	0.95
Per cent of insured families with net costs of $45 or less:					
Family income under $2,000..	178	38.2	4.01	3.64	1.10
Family income $2,000–$3,499.	340	32.9	2.92	2.55	1.15
Family income less than $3,500.................	518	34.7	2.21	2.09	1.06
Difference..................	......	5.3	5.30	4.45	1.19
Per cent of families whose total health outlay was less than 5% of their income:					
Families with some medical debt.................	417	36.7	2.85	2.36	1.21
Families with no medical debt.	2,341	62.8	1.08	0.99	1.09
All families................	2,758	58.9	1.11	0.93	1.19
Difference..................	......	26.1	2.78	2.56	1.09
Per cent of families whose net dental costs were less than 20% of net total costs (for families with some net total costs):					
Family income less than $5,000.................	1,681	71.1	1.26	1.11	1.14
Family income $5,000 or more.	869	53.2	1.65	1.69	0.98
All families................	2,550	65.0	1.20	0.94	1.28
Difference..................	......	17.9	1.80	2.02	0.89
Gross costs per family:					
Rural farm families..........	431	$177.61	15.60	11.45	1.36
Urban and rural nonfarm families.................	2,323	211.52	5.90	6.42	0.92
All families................	2,754	206.21	5.80	5.71	1.02
Difference..................	......	33.91	16.20	13.13	1.23

Table B-1 (Continued)

Characteristic	Number of units	Average, per cent, or differ- ence	Estimated standard errors of estimates		Ratio of esti- mated S.E.'s
			For design used	For simple random sampling	
	(1)	(2)	(3)	(4)	(5)
Per cent of gross total costs for physicians' services:					
Uninsured families..........	(15,613)	38.8	1.56	1.22	1.28
Insured families.............	(41,037)	37.2	0.98	0.99	0.99
All families.................	(56,650)	37.6	0.84	0.79	1.06
Difference..................	....	1.6	1.80	1.58	1.14
Per cent of net to gross total costs:					
Family income under $5,000..	(30,561)	85.5	1.01	0.99	1.02
Family income $5,000 or more	(26,133)	86.3	1.15	1.07	1.07
All families.................	(56,694)	85.9	0.87	0.73	1.19
Difference..................	....	0.8	1.26	1.46	0.86
Per cent of families with no hospital insurance (among families with known net costs):					
All families.................	2,780	36.7	1.44	0.91	1.58

errors or errors of execution. There is a 2-to-1 chance that such an estimate would be within one and a half percentage points of the census figure and a 50-50 chance that it would be within one percentage point. Thus, although the limits of possible error may be rather broad, it is very likely that actual sampling deviations will be far smaller.

The computation of standard errors for estimates based on the present sample is complex because the families in this sample were geographically clustered and stratification was used in the selection of the units. For reasons which need not be gone into here, clustering and stratification of the kind employed are virtually a requirement in most sample surveys. Because of the impossibility of taking into account the full extent of stratification used in our sample design, the method which was used to estimate standard errors tends to lead to conservative results—an overestimate of the magnitude of standard errors. It should be kept in mind that standard errors are themselves subject to estimating errors and should therefore be considered as rough approximations of the limits of likely sampling deviation.

For presentation in Table B-1 we have selected sets of standard errors which we felt would be representative of most of the types of estimates presented in the substantive chapters of this report. Column 5 of the table may be of use to the reader who wishes to estimate sampling errors for estimates not covered by the table itself. For such cases, it will usually be satisfactory to compute the standard error as if one were dealing with a simple random sample, and then multiply by the "ratio of estimated standard errors" (in Column 5) for that characteristic in the table which most closely resembles the estimate for which a standard error is desired. For most characteristics (particularly for percentage estimates), use of 1.3 for this factor will be satisfactory. Standard deviations (for use in computing the sampling error of a simple random sample) are (approximately) $160 for variables involving gross medical costs per individual; $300 for gross medical costs per family; and $260 for net medical costs per family. In most other cases, data for computing sampling errors with simple random sampling are available in Appendix A.

Nonresponse Error

As was stated earlier, it is never possible to obtain interviews with every family that is randomly selected for a sample. Experience indicates that, with skill and perseverance, noninterview rates can be reduced but that efforts to reduce them run into a "diminishing returns" situation and ultimately into a core of cases in which interviews cannot be obtained. For the present study, 3,114 families were designated in the sample; interviews were completed for 2,809 families, or 90.2 per cent of the designated families. As can be seen from Table B-2, over half the 305 families who were not interviewed either refused to be interviewed or else initially agreed but subsequently broke off the interview. The number of refusals was originally much higher than the 172 shown in the table, and considerable expenditure of persuasive ability (and of time and money) was required to bring the rate down to the level finally attained. Aside from the refusals, the bulk of the nonrespondents were families in which no one was found at home on from four to ten or more calls, or families away on extended vacations. In some of these cases the families could probably have been interviewed if efforts had been continued, but the cost of obtaining these interviews would have been out of all proportion (considering other sources of error) to the reduction achieved in possible bias due to nonresponse.

Table B-2. Number and Percentage of Sample Families for Whom Interviews Were Not Completed, by Reason for Noninterview

Interview status	Number of families	Per cent of families
All sample families*..................................	3,114	100.0
Interviewed...	2,809	90.2
Not interviewed......................................	305	
Refused or broke off...............................	172	5.5
Not at home four times or more.....................	61	2.0
Away on vacation throughout survey period...........	54	1.7
Other (could not speak English, interviewer's error, etc.)..	18	0.6

* An additional 213 dwelling units were assigned which were found to be vacant at the time of the survey, transient, or seasonal dwelling units.

The estimates in the report are based on those families which were interviewed. The amount of discrepancy between them and the figures which would have been obtained had interviews been held with all the families in the sample depends, for any characteristic being estimated, on how different the noninterview families were with respect to this characteristic from those who were interviewed. While 9.8 per cent of the sample families were not interviewed, we can be quite certain that they were not so homogeneous that the failure to reach them would bias any estimate by this amount. Certainly, the interviewed families were not identical to those not interviewed with respect to all relevant characteristics, but neither were they completely dissimilar. It would probably be safe to assume, in most cases, an error due to nonresponse of not more than 2 per cent; this margin of error would appear if, where the interview cases split 50-50, those not interviewed would split not worse than 30-70, and where the interview cases split 0-100, the noninterviews would split not worse than 20-80.

We know that the noninterview rate was highest in the large metropolitan centers and lowest in rural areas. When adjustments were made for this differential loss rate, on the assumption that the noninterviewed in a given category were similar to those interviewed in that category, estimates for the total population were not appreciably affected, even for such variables as insurance coverage, where there are marked urban-rural differences. Thus, we have presented only unweighted estimates in this report.[6]

Errors of Execution

The third source of estimating errors due to sampling is, in a sense, the converse of nonresponse. Families not properly falling within the sample as designed may be included because of mistakes in the field listing of dwelling units, clerical mistakes in selecting the sample cases from these listings, or mistakes of the interviewers in locating the assigned dwelling units.

The actual dwelling units where interviews were to be obtained were randomly selected in the central office. This selection, in its last stage, was based on ordered lists made by the field staff of all the dwelling units in randomly selected small areas. These listings were all made within the month or two before interviewing began, so it is unlikely that any appreciable discrepancy could have arisen from changes in the area in the interval between listing and interviewing— particularly so, since dwelling units still under construction were listed. The listings were generally rechecked when the office staff found that the number of dwelling units listed in an area was substantially different from independent estimates (available in all cases) of the number of units in the area. Also, for one type of underlisting which is rather common, interviewers were instructed to check at the time of the interview. Finally, the completed interviews were checked as carefully as possible in the office to discover erroneous inclusions of nonsample units, and when one was found, the incorrect interview was discarded, and the interviewer was sent back to the correct dwelling unit. Despite all these precautionary measures, some mislisting and some erroneous inclusions of nonsample families undoubtedly occurred. The effect of such mistakes on the accuracy of estimates must have been slight, however.

As a further check on this source of error, a mail questionnaire was sent to all families for which interviewer reports were received. Responses to this questionnaire (received from about 40 per cent of the families) yielded no evidence that any family not properly a part of the sample had been interviewed.

[6] See the forthcoming volume by Frederick Stephan and P. J. McCarthy on sample surveys sponsored by the Social Science Research Council.

COMPARISON OF SAMPLE ESTIMATES WITH INDEPENDENTLY DERIVED ESTIMATES

It is clear from the preceding discussion that it is impossible to determine how far different the estimates made from *any given* sample survey are from the figures which would have been obtained in a complete census, without actually carrying out such a census. We can set up certain confidence intervals within which we can expect sampling deviations usually to fall. Also, we can make—as we have done—certain conjectures as to the possible influence of nonresponse

Table B-3. Comparison of Distributions of NORC Sample and Estimates Derived from Independent Sources

Characteristics of population	Percentage distribution	
	NORC, July, 1953	Census,* July, 1953
Sex:		
Male..........................	48.4	48.5
Female......................	51.6	51.5
Region:		
Northeast....................	24.8	25.8
North Central................	29.4	29.5
South........................	31.8	31.0
West.........................	14.0	13.7
Color:		
White........................	88.8	89.3
Nonwhite.....................	11.2	10.7
Labor-force participation†		
Male:		
In labor force...............	83.0	85.6
Not in labor force...........	17.0	14.4
Female:		
In labor force...............	30.1	33.9
Not in labor force...........	69.9	66.1

* Estimate based on *Current Population Reports*, ser. P-25, nos. 93 and 97, adjusted by 1950 distribution of institutional population and P-50, no. 59.

† Age 14 and older. The NORC question on labor-force participation concerned "usual activity." The Census question refers to activity during "most of last week." Since the labor-force-participation rate in July, 1953, was higher than in any other month of that year, the NORC "usual-activity" question was likely to result in a lower rate than the Census question.

Table B-3 (Continued)

Characteristics of population	Percentage distribution	
	NORC, July, 1953	Census,* April, 1953
Age, years, total:		
Under 5	11.0	11.2
5–13	17.2	16.3
14–19	8.3	8.1
20–24	5.5	6.0
25–34	14.2	15.3
35–44	15.0	14.2
45–54	11.3	11.6
55–64	8.7	8.9
65 and over	8.4	8.4
Indeterminate	0.3	
Age, years, male:		
Under 5	11.3	11.7
5–13	17.9	17.0
14–19	8.9	8.1
20–24	4.6	5.1
25–34	14.0	15.1
35–44	14.9	14.2
45–54	11.6	11.7
55–64	8.5	9.0
65 and over	8.2	8.0
Indeterminate	0.2	
Age, years, female:		
Under 5	10.8	10.8
5–13	16.6	15.6
14–19	7.8	8.1
20–24	6.3	6.9
25–34	14.4	15.4
35–44	15.2	14.2
45–54	11.0	11.4
55–64	9.0	8.8
65 and over	8.5	8.7
Indeterminate	0.4	

* Estimate based on *Current Population Reports*, ser. P-20, nos. 38, 50, 52, 53, and 55, adjusted by 1950 distribution of institutional population.

Table B-3 (Continued)

Characteristics of population	Percentage distribution	
	NORC, July, 1953	Census,* April, 1953
Number of persons in family:†		
1	13.8	19.3
2	29.5	28.4
3	19.7	20.1
4	18.2	16.0
5	10.4	8.6
6	4.2	4.2
7 or more	4.3	3.5
Residence:		
Urban	61.5	63.7
Rural, nonfarm	20.4	21.6
Rural, farm	18.2	14.7
Marital status, male:‡		
Single	21.9	23.2
Married	72.6	71.1
Widowed, divorced	5.5	5.8
Marital status, female:‡		
Single	17.4	18.1
Married	67.5	67.3
Widowed, divorced	15.1	14.7

* Estimate based on *Current Population Reports*, ser. P-20, nos. 38, 50, 52, 53, and 55, adjusted by 1950 distribution of institutional population.

† Since the NORC family definition differed from that of the Bureau of Census, it was necessary to use several rather tenuous assumptions in making the Census distribution comparable to the NORC distribution.

‡ Age 14 and older.

errors and errors of execution, but we still cannot make definitive statements about the over-all representativeness of a particular sample.

However, there is a test for a number of characteristics covered by interviews with our sample which suggests that the net effect of non-response and listing mistakes is small. Data are available for the population as a whole in the reports of the United States Census or in independent surveys made by other agencies. Comparisons show that the distributions of our sample individuals and families with respect to a number of characteristics are quite similar to the distributions

Table B-3 (Continued)

Characteristics of population	Percentage distribution	
	NORC, July, 1953	Census,* October, 1952
Occupation, male:†		
Professional...................	7.7	8.1
Farmers.......................	11.0	9.1
Managers......................	13.3	13.0
Clerical.......................	5.0	6.3
Sales.........................	5.0	5.1
Craftsmen.....................	21.5	21.2
Operatives....................	19.6	20.4
Private household..............	0.1	0.1
Service.......................	5.9	5.7
Farm laborers.................	3.0	3.4
Laborers, nonfarm.............	7.0	7.7
Indeterminate.................	0.9	
Occupation, female:†		
Professional...................	10.5	10.0
Farmers.......................	0.8	1.1
Managers......................	4.2	5.7
Clerical.......................	27.8	27.3
Sales.........................	6.7	7.2
Craftsmen.....................	2.7	1.4
Operatives....................	20.5	20.4
Private household..............	6.5	8.3
Service.......................	13.1	12.3
Farm laborers.................	4.8	5.6
Laborers, nonfarm.............	0.7	0.6
Indeterminate.................	1.5	

* Estimate based on *Current Population Reports,* ser. P-20, no. 45, and ser. P-50, no. 49.

† Age 18 and older. The discrepancies between the NORC and Census figures are due in part to nonsampling considerations. Agricultural employment is generally more prevalent in July than in October.

found in independent and far larger samples. This does not prove that *other* estimates made from our sample would stand up as well if comparative data were available from other reliable sources. That is, even if we knew that our sample was completely unbiased with respect to sex, age, education, income, birth rate, and several other characteristics, it would not necessarily follow that the sample was unbiased with respect, for example, to medical expenditures or insurance coverage.

Table B-3 (Continued)

Characteristics of population	Percentage distribution	
	NORC, July, 1953	Census,* October, 1952
School completed, years, total:†		
Under 5	8.7	9.0
5–8	31.6	34.2
9–11	20.1	17.2
Completed high school	23.1	23.9
Some college	8.0	7.6
Completed college	6.0	6.9
Indeterminate	2.6	1.1
Median	(10.3 years)	(10.1 years)
School completed, years, male:†		
Under 5	10.5	10.3
5–8	32.6	35.1
9–11	19.7	16.6
Completed high school	19.3	20.7
Some college	8.1	7.5
Completed college	7.8	8.2
Indeterminate	2.0	1.5
Median	(9.9 years)	(9.7 years)
School years completed, female:†		
Under 5	6.9	7.8
5–8	30.6	33.5
9–11	20.5	17.8
Completed high school	26.6	26.8
Some college	7.9	7.7
Completed college	4.3	5.7
Indeterminate	3.2	0.7
Median	(10.6 years)	(10.4 years)

* Estimate based on *Current Population Reports*, ser. P-20, no. 45, and ser. P-50, no. 49.

† Age 25 and older.

On the other hand, it is not likely that serious biases due to errors in listing and to noninterviews could exist without their being manifested in the form of a substantial discrepancy on one or more of the demographic characteristics just mentioned. It will be noted from Table B-3 that, in most instances where such comparison is possible, the distribution of a characteristic in our sample is remarkably close to its distribution in the population as a whole, as measured by an inde-

Table B-3 (Continued)

Characteristics of population	NORC, July, 1952– June, 1953	NOVS,* July, 1952– June, 1953
Vital rates:		
Live births per 1,000 population.........	24.3	24.6
Deaths per 1,000 population............	5.9†	9.6

* National Office of Vital Statistics, *Annual Summary for 1953*, pt. 1.

† *Ibid.*, pt. 2. The death rate for the United States includes deaths in the institutional population. The sample population did not include persons living in institutions, nor did the sample include deaths of persons living alone at the time of their deaths.

Table B-3 (Continued)

Characteristics of population	Percentage distribution	
	NORC, July, 1952– June, 1953	FRB,* January, 1952– December, 1952
Family† money income before taxes:		
Under $1,000......................	8	10
$ 1,000–$1,999.....................	11	12
2,000– 2,999.....................	14	14
3,000– 3,999.....................	17	16
4,000– 4,999.....................	15	15
5,000– 7,499.....................	21	21
7,500– 9,999.....................	7	6
10,000 and over..................	6	6
Unknown.........................	1	
Median..........................	($3,900)	($3,850)

* Figures from *Federal Reserve Bulletin*, September, 1953, Supplementary Table 15.

† The Federal Reserve Board family is a negligibly larger unit than the one used here. In instances where two related married couples were living in the same dwelling unit, the FRB counted them as one family unit. NORC counted them as two family units.

pendent study. This finding at least makes us feel somewhat more assured when we make other estimates about the population from data derived from our sample.

These comparisons were not "forced" to come out the way they did by the imposition of external quota controls in the selection of our sample. Since our sample was a strictly random one, the correspondence between estimates derived from it and estimates from independent sources cannot be an artificial consequence of the sampling procedure employed.

ESTIMATING ERRORS DUE TO NONSAMPLING FACTORS

The preceding section of this appendix dealt with errors in estimates that may have resulted from the operation of chance in the drawing of the sample, from failure to locate and interview all families selected for the sample, and from the erroneous inclusion in the sample, through mistakes made in listing or in identifying dwelling units, of families that are not properly a part of the sample. There are always opportunities for error, also, in the collection, reporting, and analysis of data. In this section, attention will be given to these nonsampling sources of error.

The validity of any response given during an interview depends on whether the respondent has been made to understand exactly what information is wanted, whether he can supply the necessary information, whether he is willing to supply it, and whether the interviewer records the information properly. Although in general we had no direct way to assess the extent to which the above factors operated to give us trustworthy information, we do have indirect evidence concerning its trustworthiness.

To guard against possible omissions in the respondent's replies, special precautions were taken to make sure that information was collected for every member of every sample family. Specific questions were asked to avoid overlooking infants, people temporarily away from home, lodgers, etc.

Validity of Data on Insurance Coverage

An extensive battery of questions was devoted to determining whether or not the family had any hospital, surgical, or other medical-care insurance. Care was taken to avoid the omission of any formal prepayment plan which the family did not think of as insurance, even though it served the same function. The respondent was urged to bring out the insurance certificate, membership card, or any other document which might provide valid information about any insurance policy. Further, he was urged to consult any other family member who might have more complete and accurate information about the family's insurance situation, and the interviewer was instructed to revisit or to telephone the family at a later date if it appeared that more adequate information could be obtained from some family member or some documentary source not available at the time of the first interview. Moreover, an explanatory letter was sent to each sample family about a week before the interviewer called, in which the family was asked to be prepared for questions about its health insurance.

All these precautions were taken because it was feared that a good many respondents would have relatively little *ready* information of the family's insurance coverage. It was possible to get documented information from certificates or membership cards concerning *all* policies or plans reported by 59 per cent of the insured families and concerning *at least one* of the policies held by an additional 12 per cent. Thus, some documentary evidence about insurance coverage was given to the interviewer in almost three out of every four of the families classified as having some insurance coverage.

Whenever there was any doubt in the interviewer's mind as to whether a given policy was one which directly insured against the cost of medical care for illness, or whether it insured only against disability and/or lost income or accidents, the interviewer was instructed to record all information about the policy that he could ferret out. No classificatory decisions were left to the interviewer or the respondent; all such decisions were made in the central office. Many reference sources were used as aids in classifying each policy on the basis of the information supplied by the respondent: governmental publications, Blue Cross and Blue Shield guides, publications of private insurance organizations, etc. These references were used, for example, to determine, in cases where the information was not clear-cut and consistent, what source of coverage a family member might be expected to have in terms of his age and sex, his insurance premium, where he worked, and other information derived from the interview. A great deal of time and effort was devoted to making every classification as accurate as possible.

Information about insurance coverage was also obtained for some of the families in the following three ways: (1) in the course of verifying information concerning all hospital admissions reported, information about the insurance coverage of the patient or his family was sometimes provided by the hospitals; (2) mail or personal calls to employers were made in a number of instances where different individuals working for the same firm gave incompatible reports about their group coverage; and (3) a more systematic telephone check concerning group coverage with employers in selected areas was made.

Information obtained in the first of these three ways for perhaps 10 per cent of the families led to a modified classification only rarely and tended to confirm the accuracy of our classifications. The second kind of check was used rather infrequently, because the time and cost involved were prohibitive. Considerably more effort was put into the third type of check. In this connection, an attempt was made, first, to obtain information from the employer or union for all employees in the Chicago part of the sample who claimed to be carrying insurance through their place of work. The information given by the employer generally confirmed the classification of the case that would have been made without the check. Consequently, it was decided that it would not be worthwhile to check by phone on family members who had been reported as carrying group insurance. Our impression is that we may have slightly underestimated the extent to which individuals are covered by two or more plans or policies through the same or different work-groups because respondents did not always know that some family members were actually covered by several group contracts. Further, we have occasionally misclassified the type of insurer— particularly, we have mistakenly classified plans as "group, independent" where they are actually underwritten by an insurance company and should have been classified as "group, private," but the basic fact remains that almost all individuals who were classed as covered by group hospital insurance of some type unquestionably were so covered by at least one group plan.

A more extensive telephone check was made to determine the accuracy of some respondents' reports which indicated that a family member who was working full-time for a private employer or for government was not covered by group insurance through that employment. Checks were attempted with the employer or with the union for all such individuals residing in the following seven areas:

1. New York–Northeastern New Jersey metropolitan area
2. Chicago metropolitan area
3. Los Angeles metropolitan area
4. Philadelphia metropolitan area
5. Richmond, Virginia, metropolitan area
6. Eau Claire County, Wisconsin
7. Lincoln County, West Virginia

Since about 20 per cent of our total sample (and an even larger percentage of all employees in the sample) resided in these areas, this subsample constituted an adequate test. We were able to obtain information from the employer about the employee involved in approximately 75 per cent of the subsample cases. In approximately 95 per cent of these cases where employer information was obtained, our classification of the case on the basis of information supplied by the respondent would have been essentially correct. In the remaining 5 per cent of the cases, we would have classified someone who was actually covered by group hospital insurance as not covered. Considering the fact that almost three-quarters of all employees and their dependents were classified as having insurance, and considering the pattern of underreporting which was found, it is scarcely possible that more than 2 per cent of the individuals in the sample who were classified as not having hospital insurance actually had group hospital insurance through their place of employment. The underestimate for the sample due to this factor is probably considerably less than 2 per cent.

NORC and HIC Estimates

In general, the estimates of insurance coverage derived from the present survey are reasonably close to those made by the Health Insurance Council. Since the Council's estimates are based on surveys of insurers rather than of those insured, the two sets of estimates are completely independent methodologically. The comparison of the estimates appears in Table B-4.

It is impossible to account definitively for the discrepancies. The following four factors could have entered:

1. The NORC sample was restricted to the civilian noninstitutional population. Hence, the population total used in computing the coverage estimates excludes the population living on military reservations and within institutions. The HIC estimates include these groups. Conceivably, a small part of the discrepancy could be due to coverage in the population groups excluded by NORC.
2. Some NORC respondents who were actually covered by hospital insurance may have failed to report this fact.
3. The insurance companies surveyed for the HIC estimates may have overestimated the number of individuals whom they covered. This might be due to an underestimate of the extent to which two or

more group contracts or nongroup policies issued by an insurer cover the same individuals. Also, an overestimate might have resulted from a lag in the processing of lapsed policies or from a number of other factors.

4. Sampling errors may have led to an underestimate by NORC (although it is just as likely that errors due to sampling alone would have led to an overestimate).

Table B-4. A Comparison of National Estimates of Hospital Expense Protection, Continental United States, July 1, 1953

Insurer	Number of persons insured, millions	
	NORC estimate	HIC estimate*
Blue Cross......................	41.4	41.6†
Group private....................	27.3‡	31.5
Nongroup private................	19.4‡	23.5
Independent and other............	10.0	8.2†
Total.......................	98.1	104.8
Less estimated duplication......	10.0	9.7
Number of individuals..........	88.1	95.1

NOTE: Although our survey method permitted us to secure directly an unduplicated count of persons with hospital-expense protection, we are also able to present figures which include duplication for the purpose of this comparison. Duplications within and between insurers are both included.

* Midyear figures were estimated by taking an arithmetic mean of the HIC estimates for the end of 1952 and the end of 1953.

† To make HIC figure comparable to NORC figure, coverage under "hospital plans sponsored by medical societies" and Connecticut Hospital Service were included under "independent and other."

‡ This estimate has been raised by 0.1 million in order to compensate for duplication in the HIC figures resulting from medical-society-approved hospital plans underwritten by private insurance companies. This adjustment is completely arbitrary, since no one covered by such a plan may have been in our sample. But the adjustment is necessary to make the estimates comparable, since NORC would haveclassified such coverage only as "independent and other."

The excess in the NORC estimate of coverage under independent plans is probably due largely to misclassifications. Some respondents were unaware that their company or union plan was underwritten by an insurance company. Although in classifying such cases we generally checked a number of published sources to determine whether the plan was in fact self-insured, it is quite likely that we made enough errors to account for a substantial part of the excess. Thus, about a million and a half individuals in the "independent and other" category could well be transferred to the "group, private" category.

The largest discrepancy which we are at a loss to explain appears in the "nongroup private" category. This is the type of coverage of which the insured persons might be expected to be most aware. In general, application has to be made for such insurance, and the payment of premiums involves some initiative on the part of the insured. It is thus hard to believe that any large number of respondents could have failed to report the typical nongroup hospital policy. Part of the discrepancy may be explicable in terms of a restricted type of health policy. Both HIC and NORC theoretically classified as hospital insurance certain disability policies which provide extra benefit payments if the insured is hospitalized. This hospital benefit generally runs around two or three dollars a day for a limited period while the individual is hospitalized. Since this is the total provision for hospital expense under the policy, it seems likely that some respondents would be unaware that such a policy is classed as hospital insurance. Actually, this type of policy constitutes a negligible proportion of the policies we have classed as "nongroup individual." But, conceivably, these policies are fairly widespread and are represented more fully in the estimate used by HIC. Since we know of no estimate of the prevalence of this type of coverage, we are unable to assess the extent to which this factor may explain the discrepancy.

The very close proximity of our estimates of Blue Cross coverage to that used by HIC does lend some support to the accuracy of the family-survey estimates. Since the Blue Cross figures are least likely to be influenced by duplications, it is probably the most reliable estimate from either source. With respect to the other types of insurance, the fairly close correspondence between the independent sets of estimates suggests that the classification of cases on the family survey was probably accurate enough for most purposes.

We shall not treat the comparisons between the estimates of surgical-insurance coverage here, because the results are nearly identical with those for hospital insurance. The NORC and HIC estimates of Blue Shield and Blue Cross surgical coverage are nearly identical. The NORC estimates for both types of private surgical insurance are lower than those used by HIC by about the same amount as were the hospital estimates. The NORC estimate of surgical coverage under independent plans is in all probability too high, for reasons stated earlier.

On the basis of the various checks we have made, we can conclude with considerable assurance that our information about insurance coverage is, on the whole, reasonably accurate. The insurance coverage of some individuals in the sample was misclassified, but we have good reason to believe that the vast majority of individuals were properly classified. There is probably only a slight distortion, due to misclassification of insurance, in our estimates of differences between insured and noninsured or between individuals covered by different types of insurer.

Validity of Data on Hospitalization

Respondents' reports about the hospital experiences of members of their families were independently checked on the basis of data supplied directly by the hospitals, Blue Cross, and private insurance companies. Each family that reported having had a member who was a bed patient in any hospital during the survey year was asked to sign a form which authorized the hospital to provide us with information about that hospitalization. In consequence of this arrangement, we were able to obtain validating information covering 87 per cent of the hospital admissions reported by the families. The information supplied by the hospitals was completely independent of the information supplied by the respondents, since the respondents' information was not given to the hospitals on the request forms sent them.

Most of the discrepancies between the respondents' reports and the hospital records were relatively small, although there was some slight net tendency to overreport the amount of hospital bills. But in all cases the data derived from the hospitals or insurance records were accepted in preference to the data supplied by the respondent. Thus we can be quite confident about the accuracy of the data bearing on 87 per cent of those families who reported hospitalizations.

In 96 per cent of the cases concerning which data were obtained from hospitals, the respondent's report that a given hospitalization had occurred within the survey year was confirmed. On the other hand, in this validation check, an additional 4 per cent of hospital admissions was discovered—individuals were found to have been admitted to hospitals more times than they had reported; they had not reported that they had been discharged and readmitted during a relatively short time.

This procedure gave no check on the validity of a respondent's report that a given family member had not been hospitalized at all during the survey year. On the basis of pretest experiments set up, in part, to test on the reporting, and from a health study made in Boston in which we had access to records of the hospitalizations of the people in our sample, we can estimate that, at most, 5 to 10 per cent of the actual total admissions in our sample were not reported, but, in all probability, this underreporting was closer to the lower of these figures.

Validity of Data on Medical Expenditures

The accuracy of the data concerning medical expenditures and the utilization of medical facilities were largely dependent on the adequacy of our informants' memories. It was necessary for the informant to supply the interviewer with data concerning the experience of his family over the entire year. Every effort was made to get the informant to check any records he might have concerning his experiences with medical care during the year. In many instances, bills, check stubs, and other records were referred to; but in many other instances, no records were easily available, and so we had to depend on the recall of the informant or other people with whom the informant might consult.

Although it is well established that people tend to forget their minor illnesses rather rapidly, there is evidence that their recall of more major medical conditions is quite accurate. We have good reason to believe that informants seldom forgot to report relatively expensive conditions and that they seldom reported as having received during the survey year medical care that they had actually received prior to that year. Thus there is little reason to assume that many families have been seriously misclassified in terms of the medical care for major illnesses received or the expenditures for that care.

It seems extremely likely, on a priori grounds, that any particular family slightly overstated or understated its expenditures for minor conditions. The informants for some families unquestionably failed to report the one or two physician's calls for a minor respiratory infection or a childhood disease which had occurred several months earlier, while other informants may have mistakenly reported that certain minor-illness care was received during the preceding 6 months when it was in fact received earlier. While these minor reporting errors could conceivably affect aggregate estimates to some extent—for instance, if there were more underreporting than overreporting of minor illnesses, on the average—they unquestionably had only a small effect on distributions of families or individuals; where individuals or families were categorized by the level of costs incurred, it is unlikely that the misplacement could be by more than one category because of them. Thus, the general shape of a distribution by level of costs incurred must usually be reasonably accurate, even though the median of that distribution may be slightly too high or too low.

As has been stated earlier, a major purpose of the survey was to enable us to make comparisons between different subgroups of the population. Even though the absolute size of an estimate of the average experience for any subgroup may be somewhat in error, there is no reason to assume that the relative size of the averages for different subgroups has been distorted. It seems likely that these errors concerning minor expenditures that we have presumed to occur are practically equally frequent in the various subgroups, thus leaving the comparison between subgroups relatively unaffected.

We base our belief in the essential accuracy of the information we used in deriving these estimates partially on the care taken in designing the interview. The interview contained a number of prods to the respondent's memory, which were designed to help him recall various categories of expense and utilization. There were also a number of internal checks within the interview, designed to make sure that the respondent had not underreported or overreported medical care received by his family.

The devices used in the questionnaire were derived from experience in extensive pretesting of the interview schedule. In one of our pretests, we selected families about whose medical experience we had accurate information from records. It was, of course, necessary to restrict this pretest to families who were likely to have obtained all their medical care from a relatively small number of sources. Thus, we interviewed mainly families living in small towns where there was access to only a small number of different sources of care, and families who were enrolled in group-practice plans. We checked the information given to us by the families against physicians' and hospital records of the care received by the respondents. We noted, for instance, that there was some tendency to forget about care for minor, long-standing conditions, because this care was taken for granted. We thus incorporated specific questions to ensure recall of this kind of care. We noted further that care for minor injuries resulting from accidents tended to be omitted, so the questionnaire was modified to correct for this problem. Additional modifications of the interview schedule along similar lines were also made on the basis of this pretest experience.

We learned from the pretest that hospitalizations and treatment for expensive conditions were seldom forgotten. But there was a tendency to forget conditions which required a minimum of care.

Since the cases selected for inclusion in the pretest had been chosen in such a way as to maximize the interviewing problems involved, we felt that we could put considerable reliance on these results. For instance, cases were selected in which the family had had heavy medical bills immediately prior to the survey year but little expense during the survey year. We found practically no tendency to telescope these earlier expenses into the survey year. We chose other families which had had heavy expenditures near the beginning of the survey year, and here, too, we found that the family was able to place its expenditures in the proper time period. On the whole, this rather extensive pretesting gave us confidence in being able to assess the level of medical expenditure of any given family, with only a relatively small margin of error.

ESTIMATING PROCEDURES

Certain features of the estimating procedures employed in processing the data need also to be taken into account in evaluating the findings of the study.

1. For various reasons, which need not be gone into here, information about expenses incurred by families for "minor illnesses" was obtained only for the 6-month period immediately preceding the interview, whereas information about "major illnesses" was collected for a full year preceding the interview. In combining the two types of information to find out how much all medical expenses amounted to for the full year, the figures for minor illnesses were doubled. Thus, half the minor-illness costs, or 7½ per cent of total medical costs during the survey year, as shown by the tables in this report, were estimated on the assumption that, for the group of families as a whole, minor-illness costs incurred during the first half of the year would have been about the same as they were during the second half of the

year. This assumption seems more reasonable for the sample of families as a whole than for any particular family. For example, the fact that a given family had no minor medical expenses during the second half of the year does not necessarily mean that it had none during the preceding half-year. Conversely, a family that did have some minor medical expenses during the second half-year might have had none during the first half. Although both types of error would appear in the records of the families when separately examined, they might tend to cancel out in the summary statistics.

The definitions of the terms "major illness" and "minor illness" employed in the study were such that this method of handling expenditures for minor illnesses would not at all affect the accuracy of our cost estimates for hospital, obstetrical, and dental care; it would affect only very slightly expenditures for surgical care and for care included under the *Other Medical Costs* category in the tables; its chief effect would be on the estimated costs of medicines and of *Other Physicians' Services,* which were chiefly physicians' charges for home and office calls. On the basis of some empirical data available to us, and certain a priori assumptions which seem reasonable, we feel fairly certain that the *maximal* effect of this procedure on estimates of total family expenditures would not exceed 2½ per cent. In terms of dollars, this would mean, at most, an error of $5 (probably an inflating error) in the estimated average expenditure per family ($207).

The distributions of families among expenditure categories were also affected by this estimating procedure. For example, if we could have collected through the interviews information about minor-illness costs for the full year, the proportion of families or individuals appearing in the tables as having no medical costs at all would undoubtedly be lower, although the proportions having no hospital, obstetrical, and dental costs would remain the same. The proportions making no expenditures during the year for "surgical care" and "other medical services" would be only slightly reduced. In interpreting the tables showing the distribution of individuals or families by levels of cost, it would be well to combine the no-cost category with the next category and thus substantially reduce the unreliability due to this factor.

2. In a few cases where sufficiently specific cost information was not obtained in the interview, or where cost information was not obtained at all, the cost figures were estimated, if possible, in the course of processing the data. In some of these instances, the respondent had

not yet received a bill for medical services rendered. In other instances, the bill had been received, but the respondent could not recall the amount of the bill. In other cases, where the bill had been received and the amount was remembered, the costs for more than one individual or for more than one type of medical service were lumped together. In still other instances, the services reported as having been received by the respondent's family were rendered under some kind of prepaid group-practice plan which did not assess charges to its members on a fee-for-service basis.

In all these cases, an effort was made, in processing the interview reports, to arrive at what seemed to be a reasonably close estimate. Estimates were based on other data available in the reports—the amounts and kinds of care received, the individuals receiving this care, the period of time over which it was received—plus information available to us as to the prevailing rates in the respondent's community. Estimates were made only when they could be made with a fair degree of assurance. Where this was not possible, the case was assigned to the "indeterminate" category on this particular item. In the analysis, then, costs of the services received by these "indeterminate" cases were assumed to be the same as the average for the same kind of service for people incurring known costs for that service. An individual or family with unknown costs was generally assumed to have incurred the same costs as other individuals or families in their own subgroup within whatever classification was used in that particular table (income, age, etc.). The effect of this estimating procedure was somewhat to understate average costs in each category of service, especially total gross costs, since in most instances the "unknowns" were people who received relatively large amounts of medical care.

3. All the estimates made in this report are "ratio" estimates.[7] For example, the estimate of the total number of people covered by insurance was derived by computing the percentage of the sample which was covered and multiplying that percentage by the Census Bureau's estimate of the total population in July, 1953. Similarly, the estimate of total personal consumption expenditures for medical care was derived by computing the mean expenditure per family in the sample and multiplying that mean by the Census Bureau's estimate

[7] See Hansen, Hurwitz, and Madow, *op. cit.*, for a discussion of this type of estimate.

of the number of families in the country at that time. This form of estimate was unquestionably the most reliable, considering the conditions of this survey.

4. It will be noted that the number of cases classified as "unknown" in the tables showing distributions by level of cost for individuals is sometimes smaller than the corresponding figure in tables showing the distributions for families. These differences are due to the fact that, after the family data were processed, additional information was obtained from hospitals and other sources, making it possible to transfer numbers of individuals out of the "unknown" classification. It was not felt worthwhile to reprocess the family data at that time, since, on the whole, the differences in the estimates that would have resulted from these changes would have been extremely minor.

DEFINITIONS

The concept of direct personal expenditures used in this study is similar to that used by the Department of Commerce in its Personal Consumption Expenditures series.[8] The main conceptual difference is that the Department of Commerce classed as personal expenditures those expenditures for medical care that were made by nonprofit organizations, whereas they were not so classed by us. In practice, this difference is of little consequence, since it seems fairly certain that in the Commerce Department's figures only the estimates for hospital-care expenditures include any appreciable expenditures by nonprofit organizations; because of the way the figures are derived, it is dubious whether expenditures from public sources are substantially represented in the estimates for other types of care. The concept of personal expenditures used in the present study is more nearly identical with that used in the private-expenditure series of the Division of Research and Statistics of the Social Security Administration and in the consumer-expenditure surveys made by the Bureau of Labor Statistics. These two organizations exclude expenditures for services by private philanthropic organizations.

---

[8] It should be noted that most analyses of medical-care expenditures are based on the Personal Consumption Expenditure series. See, for instance, the many publications on this subject by Frank G. Dickinson, Director of the Bureau of Medical Economic Research of the American Medical Association (Bureau Bulletins 66, 72, 87, and many others).

Family

A family consisted of one person or a group of people living together and *related* to each other by blood, marriage, or adoption. However, when there were two related married couples living in a single dwelling unit, each married couple and its unmarried children were treated as a separate family. Any person who was unrelated to anyone else living in his dwelling unit (e.g., lodger or servant) was considered as a separate family.

Region and Size of Locality of Residence, Occupation, Industry, Class of Worker

The definitions used in the 1950 Census of Population were used for this survey. Details of these definitions can be found in the reports on the 1950 census.

Income

This is the total family cash income before taxes during the 12 months preceding the date of interview. Income from wages, salaries, own business or farm, professional work, trade, pensions, rents, welfare agencies, unemployment compensation, alimony, regular contributions from friends or relatives, dividends, interest, and similar sources was included. Income in kind was excluded.

Insured Family

Unless otherwise specified in the table, an insured family was one where at least one individual family member was covered on the day of the interview by insurance specifically designed to cover the costs of medical care for illness. Thus policies which covered only the costs of accidents and policies under which the size of the benefits depended solely on the length of the period of disability or income loss (from either illness or accident) but not on the medical care received were, for the purpose of this classification, not classified as health insurance. A family was classed as insured if one or more family members was covered by a hospital, surgical, or other medical policy covering expenses incurred in connection with illness or if one or more family members was covered by a policy covering medical-care expenses in connection with particular illnessess, as for instance a poliomyelitis policy, a "dread-disease" policy, or a major-medical-expense policy. In addition, families where someone was covered by a disability policy under which additional benefits were paid (usually half the daily disability payment, i.e., around $3 per day) for each day spent in a hospital (or with home nursing) were also classified as insured. Actually, in about 97 per cent of the families classified as "insured," at least one family member was covered by the usual type of hospital-insurance policy, where the size of the benefits received is in part, at least, based on the size of the hospital bill.

Type of Insurer

This classification is almost identical with that of the Health Insurance Council. The main difference is that NORC classified hospital coverage under Connecticut Hospital Service and Blue Shield plans offering hospital benefits (e.g., California Physicians Service, Oregon Physicians Service, and Washington Physicians Service) as coverage under "independent plans," while the Council classified this coverage under Blue Cross. NORC classified coverage under medical-society-approved surgical plans underwritten by private insurance as Blue Shield only, while the Council classified this coverage under both Blue Shield and private insurance and then deducted for the duplication involved.

Another difference is one of practice rather than of definition. Owing to inadequate information, NORC classified some individuals actually covered by group private insurance as being covered by "independent plans." This particular type of misclassification could hardly enter into the Health Insurance Council estimates at all.

Hospital Admissions

Since the hospitalization data used in this report is based primarily on hospital records, a utilization of hospital facilities was considered as an admission if the hospital involved so classified it. The general criteria used to distinguish an admission (inpatient care) from outpatient care are the occupancy of a bed and the maintenance of a hospital chart.[9]

In the case of a normal delivery where the mother and infant are discharged at the same time, the infant was classed as not having been hospitalized at all and was assigned no hospital charges in our

[9] See American Hospital Association, *Handbook on Accounting, Statistics, and Business Office Procedures for Hospitals*, Chicago, 1950, sec. 1, p. 9, for details. NORC attempted to follow AHA procedure as closely as possible.

processing. All charges were assigned to the mother. In cases where the infant stayed in the hospital after the mother was discharged (primarily premature infants), the infant was classified as having been admitted to the hospital. When information was available as to the date the hospital considered the infant as having been admitted, the length of stay and hospital charges were computed on that basis. Where that information was not available or where the infant remained in the newborn infant nursery (and therefore was not classed as an admission by the hospital), the infant was classed in the present study as having been admitted on the day the mother was discharged, and length of stay and the allocation of hospital charges were computed accordingly.

Gross Costs

A discussion of the basis of classification of costs appears in the footnotes to Table A-13 of this report. Although the notes to that table are concerned with the classification of physicians' charges, the discussion there is relevant to the categorization of all charges.

The following excerpt from the processing instructions used for this survey further clarifies the categorization of gross costs:

1. Surgery is defined as all cutting procedures or setting of fractures or dislocations. Exception: Costs for Cesarean delivery and circumcision are coded as obstetrics.
2. Obstetricians' fees include all charges reported in connection with delivered pregnancies; that is, prenatal care and delivery fee, irrespective of when in the survey year the baby was born. They include all charges in connection with pregnancies terminated by miscarriage and they include all charges by physicians in connection with current pregnancies.
3. Other physicians' fees include all charges made by physicians or osteopaths for nonsurgical, nonobstetrical care. (Include anesthetist's fee here.)
4. Hospital bills: Wherever possible, use verified information. Include outpatient clinic visits in a hospital under "other physicians."
5. Medicines costs are costs for drugs, prescriptions, etc. bought at a drugstore rather than drugs received at the hospital and billed for by the hospital or supplied by the physician and billed for by him.
6. Other medical expense includes special nursing, charges by chiropractors, etc., physical therapy, optical expense, cost of appliances such as crutches, hearing aids, wheelchairs, etc.; fees charged by laboratories for special tests or X-rays (i.e., when the doctor gives the test or X-ray and the doctor bills the patients for it, the costs should be coded as "other physicians' costs").
7. All charges by dentists, including dental surgery, are coded as dental.

Insurance Benefits

Only benefits from insurance designed specifically to cover expenses incurred in connection with illness were included here. Thus, benefits from straight accident insurance, disability insurance, or life insurance were excluded. Benefits from the usual types of hospital, surgical, or other medical-care insurance as well as benefits from poliomyelitis, "dread-disease," or major-medical-expense policies were included under insurance benefits. Thus, if a person received a payment designated to cover medical-care expenses under the accident clause of a policy which also was designed to cover expenses incurred in connection with illnesses, this payment was here classified as an insurance benefit.

Net Costs

"Net costs" are "gross costs" minus "insurance benefits," as defined above.

INDEX